Introduction

The history of the Fordson tractor can be traced back to 1915 when Henry Ford experimented with agricultural tractors, which resulted in the production of what became the Fordson model F tractor. The First World War accelerated initial production of the tractor which was imported by the British government to assist in food production towards the end of the war. Early imports weren't badged as Fordsons, but were known as MOM's, after the Ministry of Munitions responsible for their importing and leasing them to farmers.

Henry Ford applied the same manufacturing principles to the tractors as he did for his cars and this resulted in the Fordson becoming the most popular tractor available for many years, due to low production costs which were passed on to the customer.

Manufacture of the model F took place at Dearborn and Cork in the Republic of Ireland during the 1920s, with an improved tractor known as the model N being introduced in Cork in 1929. Production continued here until 1932 when the famous Dagenham plant in England started up.

With improvements the model N was produced through the difficult years of the 1930s and remained in production throughout the Second World War.

Peacetime saw the introduction of the popular Fordson E27N Major which

brought more power, later models also offering Diesel as an option. At this time the Ford Motor Company worked in conjunction with Ransomes, Sims & Jefferies to offer a package of power matched implements to the range. The 1950s saw the introduction of one of the most popular tractors of its day, the Fordson Major Diesel, followed by the Power Major and Super Major derivatives which continued in popular demand until production ceased at Dagenham in late 1964.

The popularity of Fordson tractors in use, both in agriculture and industrial conversions has led to them being equally popular to collectors and many examples are to be seen around today. ∎

Fordson Icons

Published by

KELSEY PUBLISHING GROUP

Printed in England, United Kingdom by William Gibbons of Willenhall, West Midlands on behalf of Kelsey Publishing Limited, Cudham Tithe Barn, Cudham, Kent TN16 3AG
Telephone: 01959 541444 Fax: 01959 541400 www.kelsey.co.uk

Designed by: Helen Blunt, Paul Silk and Rob Terry
First edition ©2010 Kelsey Publishing
ISBN 978-1-907426-03-2

With thanks to:

Andrew Hall, Peter D Simpson, Matt Bryne, Chris McCullough, Jonathan Whitlam, Bob Weir, Kerry Thornhill, Geoffrey Leigh, Peter Love, Roger Trethewy, Joseph Lewis, Derek Badham, John Allsop, Leslie Alexander, Ryan Baker, Keith Morton, Gary Connolly, Toby Ritchie, Peter Squires, Arthur Bliss, Alan Turner, Darrell Williams, Terry Hanlon, Thomas Bebb, Michael Mullen, Dave Beare, Alan Watson, Gary Boyd-Hope, Tim Starkey-Smith, Michael O'Regan, Vernon Wyke, Alan Thompson. Also a big thanks to the owners of all of the tractors featured in this publication.

Contents

6 Fordson MOM and Model F
90 years on at the FFA Showcase
in 2007

8 Rusty from France
Fascinating vineyard conversion

10 Hedgerow rescue
Fordson N

12 They've been together
A Fordson N working for
70 years on one farm

14 Yellow Fordsons
Have we found the story
behind these tractors?

18 Clyde Valley Classics
Model N collection

21 A happy N'ding
Restoration with a female touch

24 Half track, full works
Standard Fordson halftrack restoration

27 Chaseside the Company
Looking back at this
pioneering company

32 Get her to the church
(Once the tractor is restored!)

34 A tale of two diesels
Standard N Perkins power

37 A War AG Fordson
1941 workhorse

38 Brockhouse conversion
Very interesting barn find

42 The English Standard
Not as standard as you may think

44 E27N
Buyer's Guide

52 Born Again E27N
Restoration story

55 Orkney E27N
Working life on the Islands

60 A period setting
A Timewarp restoration

63 Industrial E27N
Ford Factory workhorse

64 E27N restoration
A family affair

66 E1A restoration
Saved at last

69 Fordson Major Diesel
Buyer's Guide

75 Changing colour
Massey man turns blue

78 Romantic resto
A family project

80 New and blue
Articulated Major

82 Hudson Kiwi
A rare conversion

84 Major vineyard
Earning its keep

86 Fordson Power Major
One nobody wanted

88 Wood working Fordsons
From pigs to tractors

90 Super Major restoration
'It's for my dad'

92 All about Eve
FMF8 Major conversions

96 Anniversary project
Power Major restoration

98 Super Dexta
Buyer's guide

102 A dexta challenge
First restoration

107 Family affair
A teenage restoration

110 Dexta halftrack
Rare restoration

112 Aboard a Doe
Test driving the big one

115 Designer Dextas
4WD conversion

119 Easy does it
Doe restoration

130 John outdoes doe
Meet the 170hp beast

132 Double Dexta
A mini Triple-D

134 Major electrical connections
Still at work!

136 History of a ploughman
A unique record

139 JCB MK1
The Major-based machine

142 Bob's Trio
The Fordson fleet

145 Major scrapers
Working in the muck

The Fordson MOM and Model F 90 years on

John Metcalfe from North Yorkshire aboard his 1924 Fordson Model F, which he has owned for four years. This tractor came out of a Minnesota dealer's showroom in good order as an early restoration, and it is John's intention to restore it fully, as there are one or two small problems with it.

At the 2007 FFA Showcase, Newby Hall, Ripon, the line-up of Fordson Model Fs was impressive. The event commemorated 90 years of this famous pioneering unitised tractor, built by Henry Ford and his team. Many rare machines were on show, including John's MOM which made its debut appearance.

Colin Dickinson's 1922 Model F Trackson conversion is a delight to see and shows how Henry Ford's creation could be easily adapted.

This 1917 Fordson MOM tractor fitted with a Ford replacement engine was in a sorry state when it came up at a Dorset auction in 2006. John Metcalfe said it was too good an opportunity to miss, and so he duly became the new owner. John fully restored it to the highest standard, the work lasting throughout the winter of 2006-7.

John's MOM tractor was supplied new under the Lease Lend Scheme by T. H. White Limited in 1917 to the Wiltshire area.

The engine serial number of the MOM found over the front of the manifold on the right-hand side of the tractor is 153R. The 'R' denotes a 1918 Ford factory replacement engine. The original engine would have been the Hercules four-cylinder. The engine casting code is '818' which denotes that it was built in August 1918.

'Rusty' from France

A tractor that has been attracting considerable interest at shows across the country recently is a 1927 Fordson Model F which was delivered new to France and converted virtually straightaway for vineyard use.

The warm weather of southern France is very similar to that of the dry climate of America. In these conditions tractors often lose their bloom and paintwork, but very rarely rot as they do here in Britain. This particular tractor's uniqueness is that it is an original working machine which is going to be kept as is – hence the name, 'Rusty.'

Margaret and Derek Badham, well-known collectors of early Fordsons, were offered this tractor, as the owner who had imported it from France knew it would go to a good home. Derek takes up the story.

"When we first looked at this tractor we noticed many irregularities and peculiarities which made it unique. Looking around the machine it appears that much of the work had been undertaken to blacksmith standards, yet an automotive engineer must have undertaken some of the conversion.

ON THE STRAIGHT AND NARROW

Vineyards require very narrow tractors to work between vines, and this particular conversion is 14 inches narrower than the standard Model F. The width of the tractor to rear wheel centres is 37 inches and 48 inches to the outside of the wheels. The operator platform is a mere 22.5 inches between the mudguards. The blacksmith-manufactured mudguards are a necessity to prevent the operator from catching the lug wheels."

Other fabrication work is clearly evident when looking at the front axle, which has been cut and welded, as have the steering arms. The work looks as if it was carried out by a professional. Looking around the tractor it is evident that the clutch pedal has been modified and bent in, and the gearstick also shaped. But as Derek says, the tractor must have been designed for a very small operator as he can only just fit in the seat and to operate the Model F.

"There are quite a few irregularities over a standard F including a French cylinder head and a different magneto," observes Derek who went on to explain: "The magneto is totally different and extremely rare, it is a Swiss-made MOREL-4- magneto. There is no impulse and the spark is generated by two small condensers which give a very weak spark. The magneto is mounted where the commutator should be mounted, at the front right-hand side of the engine by the radiator fan. Once up and running the old petrol engine is very powerful, but it is very awkward to start due to the poor spark produced by the magneto."

TAKEN TO BITS

Once home Derek managed to get the

Derek says this tractor is very awkward to drive and must have been designed for a small operator. The machine measures a mere 48 inches to the outside of the wheels and the operator platform is just 22.5 inches between mudguards.

'Rusty' the 1927 Fordson Model F vineyard tractor.

Derek concluded: "We are going to keep this tractor in its current condition as it is unique. The MOREL-4- magneto has caused a lot of interest and speculation as to how and why it has been fitted. Perhaps the original magneto broke and, unlike today, it may have been hard to find an original replacement, especially high up in the mountains where the tractor worked. The simple answer may have been that this particular magneto was the best replacement available at that time. We are always interested in hearing from anyone who might know differently." ■

The magneto is totally different and extremely rare, it is a Swiss-made MOREL- 4- magneto, mounted where the commutator should be.

tractor running, but it was very rough, so it was decided to take the engine to bits and fully overhaul it. The pistons wanted re-ringing and due to the unique make-up of this tractor, which is fitted with a French head, the rings are fractionally different to the standard rings on the Model F and were unavailable in Britain. Derek contacted Thorntons in Shrewsbury, an engineering firm that tends to sell everything. Sadly, though, they had no rings available. Thorntons ordered a set to be made by a firm in New Zealand; all 16 rings were made and delivered from New Zealand to Shrewsbury within ten days of ordering.

A Hedgerow rescue

Matt Bryne tells of a project he shared with his dad

While restoring a 1935 water washer Fordson for a friend, my dad Nick Bryne was taken to see a sorry-looking 1940s N, which was definitely in hedgerow condition. Dad was interested in it but wanted to get on with the water washer.

He ended up buying it and we went and winched it on to the trailer. Once home we had to unload it. This wasn't going to be easy as the steering was seized and the front wheels were not straight, so a telescopic handler was borrowed from a local farm and we lifted it off the trailer and put it in the shed.

The cylinder head had been taken off at some point while it had been left outside and the cylinder bores had filled up with water and rusted, so the engine was seized as well: we filled up the bores with rust remover.

Dad had previously made a tool to help unseize Fordson tractors, which we used and eventually got the engine turning. After this I took the front wheels and axle

off and then stripped the engine to reveal some deeply rust-pitted bores where they had rusted around the sides of the pistons.

The engine block went to Cox and Turner Engineering's machine shop and was bored out but the rust pits were still easily visible: the only option was to put new liners in.

The engine had already been reconditioned by Ford in 1953 as it had the number T62611R stamped on the bell housing (TR for Tractor Recon). At that time the firm put new liners in, so these were pulled out and luckily we had a spare set which were the right size and were pressed back in at the machine shop. This brought the piston size back to standard (4 1/8in) and after this the engine was cleaned and rebuilt.

The clutch was stripped down and the plates were not too badly worn but the driven plates had straightened out from their original Bellville spring design so they were pressed back to their correct profile and the clutch was rebuilt. The transmission, which turned out to be a special ratio high top gear version, was then stripped, cleaned and rebuilt.

Matt Bryne presses home the liners

The finished mudguards await the paint

The wings are fitted

Ready for spraying

The next job was to rebuild what was left of the wings. We made new inner plates and used a pair of original tops and a set of brackets which dad already had, but they all needed working on before being used.

Once all of the parts were ready we riveted them together.

The tractor didn't come with a fuel tank but we managed to find a rough example on a local farm, although the baffles were loose in it and it had a few small dents.

After pulling the baffles back to their correct position - which was easier said than done - they were spot-welded back in place and the dents were pulled out and filled.

Although the steering wheel spokes were present, there was no rim so dad set about making one by rolling some of the correct diameter tubing into a circle of the right diameter and then gas-welding the join. To make the rim like the original it needed the indents for the driver's fingers to grip into, so a press tool was made and we put all of the indents in, like on the original rims. Where the old rim had rusted away the ends of the spokes were very badly rusted and thin so dad made new ends and then gas-welded it all together.

To remove the king pins from the front axle we first had to get off the cotter pins, which go through the axle beam and locate in one side of the king pin, to stop them from turning. We had to heat the nuts on the cotter pins to get them off and then heat around the pins

To remove the track rod pins and forge and then beat the pins out with a

sledgehammer. Once apart and cleaned we found that the king pins, steering pins and bushes were all well worn, so new ones had to be purchased.

Once all the old bushes had been removed and the new ones were all pressed in, they had to be reamed out to the correct size as they compress when pressed. The track rod had been bent at some point in the tractor's life so that was straightened and then we assembled the axle.

The rear wheels were 24-inch and so they were more suited to being fitted on the water washer. We got some 28-inch Fordson rear wheels of the correct age to put back on to this tractor and a pair of Fordson fronts were found to match as the rims were badly rusted through on the Dunlop fronts which were fitted.

The tyres, or what was left of them inadequate and unfortunately, as they were of the original closed centre pattern, new ones were fitted all round.

While the tractor was apart we cleaned most of the small parts in a cabinet-type sand-blaster and then painted with red oxide, while the larger parts were cleaned the tractor was sprayed green in the least amount of parts possible and then assembled. ∎

Re-boring

Nick Bryne puts on the spark plug leads

THEY'VE BEEN TOGETHER...

Chris McCullough tells the story of a Fordson and its lifetime on a farm

It is not uncommon these days for a tractor to reach 70 years of age, but for one to achieve this milestone on the same farm is quite a feat.

Paddy McEvoy says he is retired but admits he still farms on a part-time basis in Sheepbridge, County Down, in Northern Ireland. Although farming has always been in his heart his pride and joy these days is his 1939 Fordson N full wing tractor, which was 70 years old in 2009.

As a tribute to it reaching this remarkable milestone Paddy decided to restore his tractor, with original registration BZ 7504, to its former glory and that restoration was completed in early February, just before its birthday.

He said: "My late father purchased this Fordson N way back in February 1939 when it cost £90 new, which was a great deal of money in those days.

"She was bought to work and that is what we used her for. I can remember myself as a young ten-year-old boy disc harrowing land with her quite a few years ago."

During the Fordson's early years on the McEvoy farm most of her time was spent cultivating flax but she undertook many other tasks, Paddy recalls.

"My father grew a lot of flax and the

Fordson was bought primarily to harvest this crop. She also was used for ploughing, threshing and baling on the home farm and helped out the neighbours on occasion on their farms too."

For years the McEvoy Fordson carried out all the tasks asked of it with ease and became very popular with neighbouring farmers.

"Everyone knew about the Fordson," said Paddy. "The tractor did a lot of work until the early 1970s, after which we retired her to the shed as farming policy changed and she was not required anymore."

In fact, the Fordson sat in the shed for over 30 years until 2008 when Paddy decided he

Paddy McEvoy's newly-restored 1939 Fordson N – which has been on the family farm for 70 years and is now celebrating its 70th birthday.

From left, Desmond Turley, George Turley, Seamus Crossan, restorer; Andy Skillen and Paddy McEnvoy, all from Sheepbridge admire the newly restored Fordson N.

wanted to restore it for sentimental reasons.

"The Fordson was simply sitting in the shed rotting away and I wanted to have her restored to her former original condition, purely because she was approaching her 70th birthday," said Paddy.

And the man tasked with carrying out the restoration was Seamus Crossan from Poyntzpass in County Armagh, who was only too delighted to take on the project. However, he did have his work cut out for him.

"When Paddy delivered the Fordson she was in rough condition with some of the metalwork needing a lot of attention," said Seamus. "The mudguards were of particular concern as they were very worn and rotten. We decided the best thing to do was replace them with brand new ones.

"The remaining sections of metal were not too bad and just needed a rub down and a good paint spray. My major concern was actually the front axle and steering pins, which needed completely refurbishing and a bit of skilful engineering.

"The TVO engine was rebuilt with new rings and valves fitted and a new throttle linkage put in place. The clutch was reconditioned and mechanically the tractor was coming together nicely."

Paddy decided to fit his beloved Fordson N with a new set of tyres to complement the restoration.

With all the mechanical work completed and Paddy's Fordson sporting a new coat of paint and a new set of tyres all that was left for him to do was start her up.

Paddy was very proud to fit the original starting handle to his newly-restored Fordson and crank her up for the first time since her makeover.

He said: "It brought back many memories when I drove her back to my yard for the first time following the six month restoration. Seamus really did a good job on her."

Paddy's Fordson N now sits proudly in his shed beside his Garvey 2ft 6in threshing drum which the McEvoy family bought second-hand in 1960.

The Fordson and thresher worked in harmony together for many years and now they are back together in retirement.

On occasion Paddy does take the Fordson out for a sentimental drive around the farm, but he is also gearing up for the vintage show season ahead. ∎

Like most girls, the N looks good from the rear too!

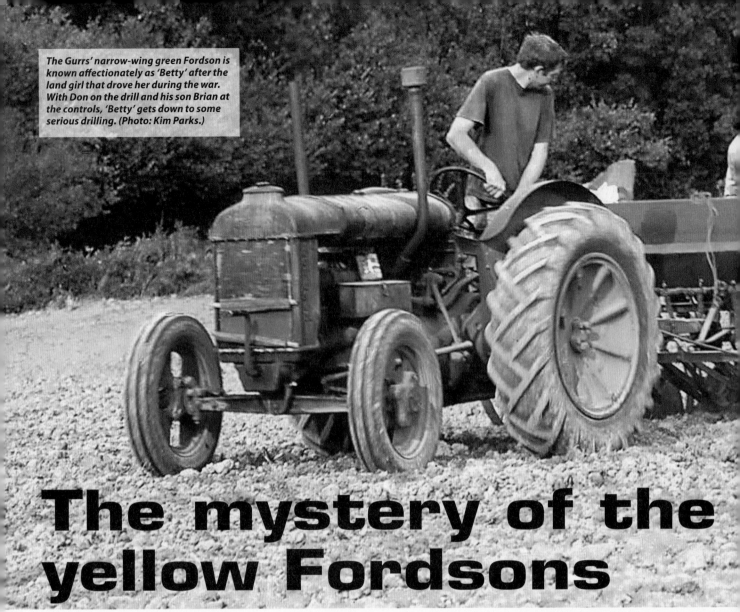

The mystery of the yellow Fordsons

The history of the Fordson tractor is well known, especially that of the Standard Fordson – or is it? Jonathan Whitlam has come across some of these popular tractors that perhaps do not quite fit into the history books.

The Standard Fordson was a very successful machine during its long production life and still remains so today as a preservation prospect. Based on the Model F Fordson that first appeared in 1917, the Model N first saw the light of day in 1928 when it was built at Ford's factory in Cork in Ireland coming with the distinctive long rear mudguards complete with toolboxes these tractors were so distinctive.

Production in Cork ceased in 1932 and building of the grey Model N switched to Dagenham in Essex, England. Several changes were made at the time, not least the change to a dark blue and red colour scheme.

1937 saw the change to bright orange paintwork and a boost in engine power and these tractors were known as the Harvest Gold Fordsons. Because of the onset of the Second World War, the garish orange gave way to green in 1939 but

Don rolling with his Perkins P6-powered Fordson Major. (Photo: Kim Parks.)

the tractor continued to be built in large numbers throughout the war until it was replaced in 1945 by the E27N Major.

FOUR MAJOR CHANGES
So far so good, the Standard Fordson went

through four major changes during its long production run and this is well documented, but where does that leave the yellow-painted Fordsons that you occasionally see at rallies and plough days? Well, I did not think much about this before; I just

Don Gurr, who first drove this tractor when it was new, is convinced his yellow Fordson is one of the government-stockpiled tractors of 1939.

1937 and Harvest Gold orange brightened up the Model N.

The less noticeable green, with wide wings, took over in 1939.

assumed that these had been painted this colour by their current owner or a previous one for some reason, perhaps for highway or industrial use. Strange though, that those in Dorset and others in East Anglia and Ireland looked as if they were painted the exact same shade of yellow – but coincidences do happen, don't they?

That's where I left it until I met Sussex farmer Don Gurr, sadly now retired due to ill health. Not so long ago Don was still actively farming near Battle in East Sussex with a fleet of Fordson tractors, including three Standards. All of these tractors had lived locally for all their lives and Don had a good idea of their history. The green wartime Fordson, for example, is called 'Betty' after the land girl that used to drive her and she still lives in a nearby village.

ORIGINAL WORKING CONDITION
In fact the only modern tractors on the farm are a Zetor 7745, a Marshall 802 and a David Brown 995 which are supported by the Fordson Standards and two E27N Majors, all of which are still used for farm work. All the three Model N tractors are in remarkable original working condition; they have not been restored in any way and are very much everyday working machines. Parts have gradually been replaced over ▶

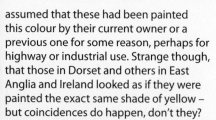

Also shown in Ireland this yellow N has the conventional exhaust stack.

Another Irish yellow machine complete with downswept exhaust. Is this one of the 1939 stockpiled Model Ns?

the years to keep them running but they have not been anywhere near a paintbrush!

The tractor that took my eye however, had to be the yellow Fordson N complete with retractable wheel strakes, and when Don told me the history of this particular tractor the pieces of the jigsaw seemed to fall into place!

As Don reminded me, back in 1939 when the war was looming on the horizon, the British Government and the Ford Motor Company had agreed a deal whereby the government would stockpile 3000 Fordson tractors in readiness for the effects of the coming conflict. When war did break out in September 1939, the 3000 Fordsons were ready and waiting for action and Don is certain that his yellow example was one of those stockpiled. Furthermore, all the reserve tractors were painted in the distinctive yellow paintwork to differentiate them from the normal production batches.

Most of the 3,000 went to contractors and large farmers who could get the best out of the tractors for the purpose of growing food and stop the country from starving into submission. Because they were worked so hard Don thinks this is why not many yellow tractors survive today – that and some have probably been repainted. Don's tractor went straight to work with a contractor in Sussex working round

The move to Dagenham brought the distinctive dark blue and red paintwork.

Don also owns an orange tractor which is in remarkably original condition – also a local tractor from new.

Light grey was the colour of the first Model N tractors built at Cork in Ireland.

the clock ploughing, the drivers working in 12 hour shifts and the tractor only stopping to refuel. Don remembers well when it arrived as he drove it himself – hence his insight into the yellow Fordson story.

CHIPPED AWAY

Now, there appears to be no documentation to back up Don's claims, though he has chipped away at the paintwork on his Fordson to see if another colour lurks underneath, but has found no evidence of orange or green paint. It seems that this Fordson was painted yellow at the factory.

Yellow also appears to have been the colour used on some Fordson machines earlier in the story of the Model N. One example preserved in Ireland for example, was built in Dagenham from parts made in Cork before Dagenham production got underway properly, and this machine

A light blue took over before production finished in Cork.

is painted a very similar yellow.

Don is convinced that the yellow Model N Fordsons, like his original example, were the government's stockpile of 1939 and if he is right then these tractors represent the very important role adopted by the Fordson tractor during the two world wars and deserve the recognition that such a feat would bring. And, just to throw another spanner in the works, the orange Fordsons are known as the Harvest Gold models – a description that, when you really

think about it, has to be stretched a bit to describe an orange livery. Yellow on the other hand, is much nearer to the colour of a harvest field! Makes you think doesn't it?

So, what do you think? Were the yellow Fordson Standards really the stockpiled tractors of 1939 or just an industrial version? Does the yellow paint have more to do with a lighter shade of orange – perhaps faded over time? Do you have anything to add to the story of the yellow Fordsons? Maybe you own one? ■

Clyde valley classics

Bob Weir gives himself a treat

The Fordson model N puts a smile on the face of any enthusiast and to come across three versions of this legendary tractor, as I did on my visit to Willie Foster's 183-acre farm at Strathavan near the Clyde Valley, was a real treat.

Most people associate Scotland's famous river with ship building and other heavy industries but just a few miles upstream from Glasgow, the mood of the countryside suddenly changes.

The Clyde Valley is a landscape of stunning scenery, rolling farmland and small mill towns - a poignant reminder that back in the nineteenth century most of the country was still predominantly rural and more than 100,000 people were employed in a thriving textile industry.

Willie originally hails from just up the road in Glenbuck, West Ayrshire, an area well-known for its open-cast mining and as the birthplace of legendary Liverpool football manager Bill Shankly.

The Fosters farmed there for several generations, dating back to the time of Queen Victoria, but in 1981 one of the mining companies made a generous offer to buy their land and the family moved to their present property on the outskirts of Strathavan.

Willie specialises in breeding cattle and currently has a herd of around 50 cows - a mixture of cross Angus/Friesian with the occasional Limousin and Hereford thrown in for good measure.

He also keeps 150 ewes and, as if this workload wasn't heavy enough, he finds time to do occasional contract baling and silage for some of the neighbouring farms.

Willie has been buying old tractors and Land Rovers for many years and has built up an impressive collection. As well as the three model Ns, he also owns a 1948 E27N that first started life as a Ford company demonstrator.

In addition, his fleet includes an early Super Major and a 1964 Super Dexta. He also has a 1978 Muir-Hill 12 and his working tractor is one of the latest Renaults.

All this begs the question: why this burning passion for all things Fordson?

He explained: "My father worked with Fordsons from an early age and I got to like them when I was a teenager."

Foster Snr was first acquainted with the N during the early days of the Second World War. Before the outbreak of the conflict tractors were comparatively few

The green model Ns were the last to be built before the introduction of the E27N. This one is a 1940 version and has been restored to a high standard.

and far between in Scotland and the majority were wearing a Fordson badge.

Despite his tender age, Foster Snr was pressed into service as part of a Government contract to increase food production to combat the growing threat from German U-Boats. This resulted in an additional 61 million acres being put under the plough, swinging the balance firmly back in Britain's favour.

Following the end of hostilities Mr Foster switched allegiance to the 'little grey Fergie' and a succession of Ferguson 35 and Massey Ferguson 135 tractors. But the Fordson stuck in Willie's memory and, when he finally got round to buying his own classic machine, the choice was a formality.

He said: "It was my brother Robert that spotted the advert for BS 2131 back in the early nineties."

When they went to Gretna to see it, there was a further surprise in store. It turned

The low-compression engine was used on the first few batches of the orange version, before it underwent a series of modifications

out that the blue 1937 model N wasn't the only Fordson up for grabs. The seller had also decided to part with a green 1940 version that had recently been restored (these green tractors were allegedly painted in this colour to avoid being

spotted by marauding enemy aircraft).

The brothers had only planned on buying one machine but the opportunity to snap up two Ns was too good to turn down. A deal was agreed and the tractors were soon heading north on the back of Willie's low-loader. They now hold pride of place at the Foster farm.

Willie admits that the provenance of the tractors is a bit of a grey area, although BS 2131 is undoubtedly an Orkney registration. (How the Fordson came to leave the islands and find its way so far south is unclear)

He reckons it is one of the last blue models to roll off the Dagenham production line before the introduction of the more distinctive orange colour scheme ▶

BS 2131 originates from Orkney and is thought to be one of the last blue models.

towards the end of 1937. For evidence, he points to the improved pto unit that was only used on post-1936 models. He admits that it is difficult to be precise about the date because at some point during its career the tractor has been fitted with a re-conditioned engine.

The blue Fordson also differs from subsequent model Ns in being equipped with a low-compression engine.

"The early tractors were all fitted with this unit that featured paired spark plugs along with a water-filled air cleaner," said Willie, adding that the performance compared favourably with the later types.

The low-compression engine was also used on the first few batches of the orange version before it underwent a series of modifications. These included tinkering with the con-rods and cylinder head in an effort to improve performance. According to Willie, these experiments had mixed results.

Fortunately, by the time of the introduction of the green model in 1940 the problems had mostly been ironed out and the new high-compression unit was fitted as standard until the tractor was finally withdrawn in 1945 to make way for the petrol E27N.

Willie added: "A more useful improvement was the switch to the oil bath air cleaner that was preferred on both the orange and green tractors." The revised cleaner was considered more reliable and easier to maintain, especially during the winter months in the days before anti-freeze.

The history of the green machine is murky, although it is believed to have come from Liverpool.

They say things often come in threes and a few months later the orange tractor was added to the collection. The history of this machine is well-known.

It was originally bought from the Lanark Fordson dealership and Willie is only the second owner from new. It spent most of its working life in Blantyre before eventually moving to nearby Crossford.

When the owner died, his son wasn't interested in keeping the tractor and was happy to accept Willie's offer. The 1940 model is a late orange example and is still in its original condition right down to the manufacturer's instruction panel.

The Fordsons spend most of the year tucked away in an outbuilding, where Willie and brother Robert have put together an impressive workshop. Until recently, he displayed them at vintage vehicle shows but "unfortunately my

two favourite events - Scone Palace and Selkirk - both take place in early September which has become one of my busiest times of the year. This means that the Ns now have to make do with the occasional spin around the yard."

When Willie does find the time to attend a show, he now prefers to take along his superb Land Rover Series One.

He said with a smile: "Although I am very fond of the tractors, the model N is a bit like a woman - too temperamental by half! You can warm them up the night before, put them on the back of a trailer, stick them on the line without any problem, then hey presto! When you want them to perform they suddenly refuse to start!" ∎

The E27N was introduced in 1945 with a petrol engine. Later models featured diesel engines, including Perkins P6 variants.

Kerry at a ploughing fun day.

A happy n'ding

Restoration projects are usually reckoned to be a male preserve but 25-year-old Kerry Thornhill begs to differ

Until a year ago my understanding of the old tractors on my dad's dairy farm went as far as skidding around the yard on the Massey Ferguson 35 scraper tractor, or power-harrowing in the blistering heat for 12 hours at a snail's pace on the Zetor Crystal. While my dad Chris has always had an avid interest in restoring classic vehicles and machinery, I never thought I would follow in his footsteps and take on a restoration project of my own.

Dad has restored various projects over the years - from his Dennis Pax Whitbread brewery lorry to his pride and joy, a Fordson P6 – but, as any farmer will tell you, spare time for hobbies and interests is virtually unheard of in agriculture.

Then, with his second Whitbread lorry waiting in the wings for restoration, he mentioned to my boyfriend Graham and I that if we restored

his Fordson N we could have it.

With no arm-twisting needed, we decided that 15 years sat in the barn was a long enough wait and it was time for the little tractor to be brought back to life. As with most restoration projects, each tractor has a story to tell and that is certainly the case with our Fordson N.

Its original owner John Wicks, a Berkshire farmer, worked the tractor on his land for many years. As a young child growing up on the neighbouring farm, my dad remembers it well. He spent many hours helping John in the workshop and also on the farm. He clearly recalls sitting on the tractor's wing at the age of 11 while John was ploughing one of the fields.

Dad and John remained close friends for many years until John sadly passed away after a fight with cancer. It was a particularly kind and thoughtful gesture that John's father Reg said he would like my dad to have the Fordson N.

In need of restoration, the tractor

was collected and unloaded into one of our barns. And there it has sat, really for as long as I can remember.

The tractor was damaged quite badly in a barn fire many years ago so before embarking on the restoration we needed to make sure the gearbox and engine would actually work. Its engine was beyond repair with a badly cracked block so we replaced it with one from an E27N that my dad had 'lying around'. We towed our sorry-looking tractor, with a washing-up liquid bottle for a fuel tank, into the yard where dad and Graham set to work turning the crank handle to see if it would fire.

For a good two hours, standing in freezing cold wind, I watched and hoped in vain as the tractor coughed and spluttered but would not run. After a break for lunch we scratched our heads, not that this would have resulted in any genius solutions on my part, and with fresh ideas in hand we got back to work. Having decided that it was the vaporiser/manifold at ▶

Day 1! Getting started.

fault, we borrowed one from an up-and-running E27N – this we are yet to return!

With the manifold fitted, and still no luck, the next step was to see if it would go if we towed it. I jumped on the P6 and began to tow dad round and round the cowshed. It felt like a Benny Hill sketch with dad bouncing this way and that on the broken seat, juggling between the fuel bottle in one hand and managing the choke, throttle and steering with the other. The whole event was highly amusing but more importantly successful. Our restoration project was to begin!

Once we had manoeuvred it back into the workshop, the Standard was stripped ready for the time-consuming task of cleaning and prepping to paint.

For me, the beauty of taking the tractor apart was that dad and Graham could explain how everything worked, much in the same way that dad learned from John some 40 years ago.

While Graham and dad worked on the more technical side of things, I occasionally found myself standing around feeling frustrated that I didn't have the mechanical knowledge and understanding to take on jobs myself. There were certainly more girly things like shopping or horse riding that I could be doing, but dad and Graham didn't leave me standing still for long and kept me busy making gaskets, sanding, painting with red oxide and getting the tractor ready to spray.

A few parts were required along the way but we managed to restore the tractor spending very little money at all. Dad

seemed to ferret around in sheds and crates and come up with all sorts of bits and pieces he had collected over the years – even a spare fuel tank. The best find, however, was at a farm sale where dad and Graham purchased a pair of original 24-inch rear wheels with good useable tyres for just £10! Getting them on to the trailer for the return journey was not an easy job. They knew they would be heavy, but heavy was not the word. They later discovered they had been ballasted with water!

With the tractor sprayed and fit to go, we test-drove it around the fields and were pleased to discover it was a high top gear gearbox. Unfortunately, it was very noisy and much to our disappointment the little tractor had to return to the workshop to be taken apart again. Graham delved into the gearbox and found a very damaged bearing, probably a result of many years of hard graft. He removed and replaced it with a bearing from a spare gearbox dad also had 'lying around.' After re-assembling

Kerry's dad and Graham fitting the engine to the gearbox.

the tractor for another test run, we were relieved that the problem was solved.

The Standard is by no means in mint condition but we have restored it as best as we can. The wings, in particular, were very twisted and split from the fire, but we managed to beat them back into pretty good shape.

My dad also made the footplates himself, which saved me the expense of purchasing new ones. It is these little touches that make the tractor all the more special to me.

A neighbouring farmer, Rosemary French, heard about our tractor and said she had just the thing for us – a Bamford Royal finger bar mower. We were thrilled to have something that we could actually use on the tractor

and when dad saw Graham and I mowing the docks in the paddock he didn't admit it but I think he had a tear in his eye as all the old memories came flooding back to him!

The little tractor now sits proudly alongside the other vehicles on the farm. My dad has always been into restoring old tractors and machines but I never realised how much fun and how rewarding it can be! Would I work on such a restoration again? I would probably say that if a vehicle held the same family history and memories as the Standard, I would definitely help out, but for now I'm happy to put my new-found mechanical skills aside.

The family history of the tractor has

made it particularly special to restore and I hope that John and Reg are up there somewhere, smiling and pleased to see their old tractor back to life again.

The Banbury Steam Fair 2008 was our first major outing with the tractor and we have since taken it to a few local events. On closer inspection of other Model Ns we soon realised that our front axle was incorrect and have since replaced it with the correct version for its year, 1939/40.

We now look forward to some more events. ∎

Kerry and her dad having their first drive.

Half-track gets the full works

Geoffrey Leigh from Holsworthy, Devon, describes rescuing a Fordson

After collecting various different types of Standard Fordsons I decided to add a crawler version to my collection, so I advertised and eventually a chap from Southampton rang and said he had a Fordson crawler with a wartime Hesford winch on the front, mounted on an axle.

These machines are called Half Tracks as they have a steerable front axle.

I arranged to see the machine. I had been told it was in a terrible condition and when I saw it I had to agree, the engine was seized and the gear lever and the worm gear had been removed so the crawler could be pulled around.

The front axle had rusted solid, all the 4x2 channel which the winch was mounted on had nearly corroded away to nothing. The steel plate fabricated front idlers had rotted away at the lower edges. The heavy 6x3in angle iron track frame had

corroded in large areas to almost nothing.

All the rear sprocket rollers had seized up and some had corroded through to the inner steel bushes. The tracks were of forged steel and in good condition, but all the link joining pins had rotted away except where they were inside the track link plates.

The only good thing was that all the cast iron and cast steel parts had not rotted and it was nearly all complete; even the Harper air brake system, which was used with trailers, was complete. On the fuel tank the original RAF stencils were still visible.

So I decided, as it was a rare RAF version, to buy it and make it a long-term project.

The crawler was eventually delivered on a low loader. It was towed off and, although the steering was seized up, there was a little amount of use in the drum brakes which act on each rear drive sprocket, so a small amount of turning was possible with the help of the tractor dragging it.

It was towed into our field in preparation for the major job of

stripping everything down.

First the winch was removed from the brackets and axle. The axle was too badly corroded so another complete axle was found. The radiator, fuel tank and manifold were all easy to remove.

The engine was the original petrol version but seized solid. When I removed the engine oil a lot of water came out, which I had expected as the crawler was left outside for many years. Then I cleaned up the engine and removed the petrol-only cylinder head and sump to see if anything could be salvaged. The bores were heavily corroded with rust and the pistons seized solid.

I had a spare Standard Fordson engine in good running order so I used it - it was a TVO version, which would make the tractor more economical to use.

I unbolted the front ring of bolts holding the gearbox in place and had a shock waiting for me. What had happened was the water had filled up the air cleaner and manifold then run past the pistons

"I had been told it was in a terrible condition and when I saw it I had to agree" – but dismantling in preparation for repair has begun.

The track frame assembly with new elements.

and filled up the sump; the water had run from the engine through the gearbox seal and corroded all the metal gear teeth and bearings above the oil level. So another gearbox had to be found.

The original gearbox was an SR red spot type, which gave a lower speed first and second gear.

The tracks were the Roadless type with the track plates and driving plates and rubber blocks between them all held together with two six-inch long half-inch diameter pins.

The track frame bolts and support bracket bolts were all so badly corroded that it was impossible to separate all the parts so the only way was to cut each cross-member bolt and separate the whole complete track and frame. This made things easier and the track was left as a complete ring.

Once all the frame was cut up and separated, new steel could be cut and fabricated. The side frames had the old idler mountings removed and riveted on to the new side frames. A new middle cross-member and rear swinging tow bar tube were remade.

The front cross-member was a complicated job to remake so the badly corroded ends were angle-ground flat and strips of metal welded around the edges. All the areas of deep pitted corrosion were cleaned out and built up with welding rods and cleaned up with a grinder.

At the time of assembly I could only find a green spot gearbox to put in, although the gear ratios are different on first and second. At the time I did not think it would matter, but when I came to drive the crawler, because of the large diameter driving sprockets and the weight of the machine, the gear ratios were too high on second gear so the crawler can only really be used in first gear.

The project of reassembly started with putting the green spot gearbox in the rear axle casting and the worm drive, axle and differential together.

The brake drums are part of the cast hub in the centre of the driving sprocket, they only needed cleaning up and the oil removing. The brake shoes were adequate to re-use but the back plates had rotted through in places where wet leaves had accumulated.

I advertised for another pair of Fordson Industrial brake back plates but with no success, so when they needed to be fitted to the axles I had to repair them. On the outside I MIG-welded tin sheet to the flat surfaces and smoothed off with filler.

The repaired brake assemblies were fitted - these are operated by a brake pedal. The rear sprockets with the brake drums were aligned on the axle shaft then the inner track frames were bolted to the three cross-members and the rear axle castings. The bottom rollers were bolted in and the outer track frame bolted to the rollers.

The rear driving sprocket is fabricated around a cast iron hub, the large diameter disc was welded in places to fill up corroded pits and ground smooth. ▶

The winch frame finally completed after fabricating new parts.

The half-track finally beginning to take shape.

The rollers were beyond repair so each one was cut with a grinding disc to release it from the steel bush inside and new rollers were made.

All the bolts on the track frames and cross-members are five-eighths diameter and the nuts are all castellated with split pins; these were all replaced with new ones.

The front idlers, which are fabricated around a central hub, were too badly rotted on the bottom to be used. Steel plate was gas-cut into four discs, which were then machined by Bill at Jarvis Engineering, High Wycombe, on a turret lathe and the centres bored out. The bolts had the heads built up with weld and new large-sized Whitworth nuts had to be found.

All the shafts and bushes in the idlers and bottom rollers were in like-new condition and still well-lubricated. The front idlers were assembled and new support brackets made; these were mounted on the frames and adjuster holes drilled in the track frames.

The tracks were another problem. The track plates are held together with two six-inch-long half-inch diameter rods with each end slotted and split open with a chisel to stop them slipping out.

All of the mild steel pins had rotted away, except the short length inside the track plate, so a large clamp had to be fabricated to hold the inner and outer plates together while each short length of pin was drilled out (not an easy job) and replaced with new pins.

The swinging draw bar hitch was in good condition as it was forged. The front end of the draw bar has a heavy coil spring and sliding rod attached to the front cross-member. The spring absorbed sudden shock loads from towed trailers on airfields.

The draw bar had corroded badly between the spring frame and the tow hitch so it was replaced. It had to be curved to fit up under the rear cross-member and this was done by pressing the bar, supported on blocks, with a large excavator bucket.

One of the original mudguards was still on the crawler so this was used as a pattern to remake the angle iron frames and tin sheet for both sides. The top edge is curved and is rolled around a steel rod. As I could not roll the edge around a rod along a curve without wrinkles I just brazed a larger diameter rod on to the top curved edge of the tin sheet to look the same as the original.

A new winch chain guard was made by using the original one as a template.

A minor problem which has appeared after the rebuild is that the gear lever sometimes jumps out of first gear so the assembly on the side of the gearbox will have to be removed. Although when I cleaned up the parts originally they looked OK, the selector balls were obviously worn. This could have been a reason why the crawler was left abandoned for many years.

The history of this crawler is known since the 1980s when Ron Marchant bought three of these Half Tracks from a yard near Guilford. He restored one, which is now in the Duxford aircraft museum. If anyone knows of any previous history please let me know.

Now that I have finished this project I am looking for another similar derelict or unfinished project! ∎

It's all over – a stunning job!

Chaseside the Company

For many, Chaseside is encapsulated by the E27N Hi-Lift loading shovel, particularly with the smaller ½ yard or ¾ yard bucket. Peter Love's father had an interest in industrial railways and as such they came across them regularly at various sites. Dover docks, particularly the west, was a place where Peter loved to see Chasesides at work along with the tractor shunters of various makes, as he explains here

This image was taken some ten years ago now on a hot sunny April day in Essex with Martin Sweetman at the controls, he very kindly manoeuvred the 'beast' around the yard. The E27N felt at home here and suited the surroundings of the late afternoon sun so well; it could have been 1949 all over again

FINDING A FORDSON F SHOVEL

In the late 1950s and early 60s, we would visit scrap yards to look at steam traction engines, rollers and WW2 gliders blowing around in the wind. On one hot Saturday afternoon in one of these yards in Berkshire, where we were walking around, I came across a great discovery. This time however, I managed not to trip over and get plastered in oil, or scratch my legs as was normal in my excitement to tell dad. When he arrived on the scene I was told it was a solid tyred Fordson F shovel and was probably a Chaseside. I hasten to say he omitted to take a picture of it.

Having a father who knows all these weird things was to be a distinct advantage in later life, but at the time other children thought I was rather odd to be interested in lots of rust!

CHASESIDE ORIGINS

I had probably been looking at one of the very first types of Chaseside loading shovels, which were produced from the early to mid 1920s by the wealthy and very clever engineer George Jackson, who was by then a Ford Model T car, commercial, tractor agent. George had been doing well after World War One when he purchased many vehicles from the various WD vehicle dumps around London, particularly Slough. He rebuilt them at his Enfield Chase premises; hence the company name Chaseside, and sold them at good profit as did others in the area.

In an effort to beat his rivals and sell more Ford stock he made a number of interesting conversions, including breakdown cranes to fit on the Model TT chassis. He then turned to the Fordson tractor and like others, created a shunter out of it to be followed by an ingenious loading shovel. It was similar in some ways to that being made in the USA at the time, but not in Europe. It was a first as such over here. It couldn't have been easy driving those very early Chaseside Fordson F shovels, particularly with the high gearing they carried. The ½ cubic yard bucket was lifted by cable and tipped by gravity. It became a very popular product in the company's line as time went on.

BRING ON THE SKIDS

From those early days the Irish N came along in 1928 and these were used as the basis for more Chaseside shovels although, at times, stock was on and off with the supply of the skid units. However this was to change when Dagenham got fully going in 1934.

Chaseside's only opposition of substance at the time was Muir Hill who also used a Fordson skid unit with their shovels and cranes and used a winding drum high up above the driver; Chaseside used this idea for a short while before going back to the rear drum unit right through WW2 until they introduced hydraulics in 1954/5. By then the company had used the E27N as the basis of its cranes and the 'new' E1A Major from 1952.

POST WAR DEVELOPMENTS

After World War Two, and with Chaseside Engineering Co working on many projects (created in 1937), expansion was helped by following the move to a factory in Hertford. Here the company benefitted from a direct link to the London mainline station at Enfield and to the London docks. The development of the cranes and loading shovels, particularly now at 2 ton capacity, continued based on the E27N.

Chaseside Engineering became the 'king' in light excavation, both at home and export markets, with good demand from many of the colonial countries. In 1949 alone approximately 5,000 cabled shovels and cranes were manufactured. Sales continued to be healthy with the Perkins diesel engines in 1950 and the 'New' Major from 1952.

THE HYDRAULIC ERA

The company's finance director Fredrick E Weatherill tried to persuade the Jackson family and other Chaseside board members to take on hydraulics after he had seen them at work while on holiday in Sweden. Here he saw a prototype hydraulic loading shovel possibly a Bolinder Munktell.

In the end Fred went his own way and first set up at the former Rifleman's Arms and yard at Tottenham, London. His 1H prototype loading shovel, based on an E27N p/p was worked by hydraulics with a trip rope mechanism for the

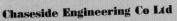

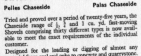

The buckets were made in ½, ¾ and 1cu yard capacities. The advert tells us that 6,000 Chasesides were in operation in the very early 1950s

Dual wheels were not uncommon for heavy work with a Chaseside, particularly with the heavyweight in mind and balance

bucket. The 1952 Weatherill 2H, the 'Real McCoy' based on the 'new' E1A Diesel Major, now had the bucket hydraulically controlled. It was still being made in the 60's, by which time it had been made in some considerable numbers.

In the meantime the Chaseside machinery construction side of the business went hydraulic in 1955 with the LM500 based again on a Fordson Major skid unit. The company still had Chaseside Engineering which they set up in 1937 and the Ford agency and used a Diamond T for heavy recovery after WW2. The LM range proved to be a great success, but the company was making many other types of construction equipment as well, including dumpers, shunters and so on.

MERGER AND TAKEOVER

The year 1959 was fateful for Chaseside; it introduced their mighty LM1000 4 x 4 loader shovel, not based on a Ford skid unit for the first time. It also merged with Blackburn, Lancashire based British Northrop that same year. Interestingly Gordon Jackson, son of the founder of Chaseside, was made MD of the construction division. Space precludes us from going into further detail, but just to say the division was to be taken over by JCB in 1968, but traces of the company finished in 1972 when the former Chaseside Load Master finished its production. ▶

The Hertford brick stacker is certainly different and needed skill in operation. I have actually seen one work in Canterbury, Kent, in 1962

Chaseside made all manner of construction equipment based on the Fordson skid unit

Seen in the early 60s is the AEC Mammoth Major MkV with Park Royal cab. The eight-wheeler is on bulk coal work with the Chaseside LM 700 hard at work loading. In the background is a Priestman excavator

Paul Tofield took this picture of Steve Richard's of Ruthin, Wales excellent Fordson N Chaseside 582 restoration

As Paul looks down on the 582 we see the full arrangements of the simple controls as everything goes on all around you. What a Health and Safety nightmare!

The Chaseside that has held the flag high in recent years and has attended a number of FFA Expo's over the years is this fine E27N 20cwt example fitted with the petrol paraffin engine

Seen at the April 2009 Cheffins Vintage Collective where the ex Raymond Walls NI Chaseside E27N was to sell for well over £3,000, which it thoroughly deserved

Steven Bolton's wonderful 1961 Chaseside LM700 hydraulic loading shovel with beet harvester bucket

This Chaseside Fordsons was rescued from a Kent scrapyard

Get her to the church

Roger Trethewy writes about the perils of a persuasive daughter

Our Fordson E27N has been in the family for 62 years; it was bought by my grandfather Samuel Pearce on July 15, 1947, the day I was born. It came from Truro Garages Ltd as a new Fordson Major Land Utility for £285 with added independent brakes at an additional cost of £11.

The tractor was used by Grandpa Pearce and his son Uncle Percy for general farm work until about 15 years ago. When my daughter Anna and her boyfriend Oliver got engaged Anna decided that she wanted to travel to the church on her late great-grandfather's tractor. I did point out to her that this tractor would need rather a lot of work done on it to make it fit for purpose, but she was very insistent.

Eighteen months before the wedding day Anna, Ollie and I started the total strip-down and rebuild process, the men taking it apart and Anna doing mainly cleaning and painting the undercoat.

Above: Before work began

Right: Anna was not afraid to get her hands dirty

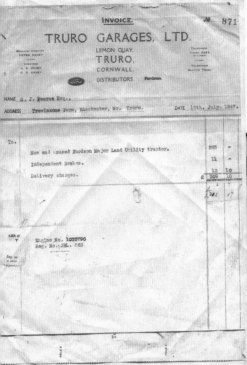

The original receipt

A bit of a mess

Work progresses

Still some way to go

The engine

There were times when we felt like giving up, such as when we couldn't start the engine, which we were building from three scrap power plants. But after a lot of back-firing we got the ignition timing right and then, much to our excitement, our Fordson sprang into life and fitted with the original back tyres and new mudguards it started coming together.

This obviously gave us the enthusiasm to carry on and, with a little more fine tuning, our Fordson was finally ready for the paint job, professionally done by Scott Yeo.

At this point we were looking forward to Anna and Ollie's wedding day except we didn't have a suitable trailer to go behind the tractor – and this is where retired contractor Jack Michell came to the rescue with the loan of a farm cart which he made

himself more than 50 years ago.

So on the morning of the wedding, with the sun shining, the Fordson E27N ribboned, the cart decorated and the bride looking beautiful, we were ready for our half-mile journey to the church, driven by Anna's cousin Wayne.

Ollie arrived with his brother Tom on his Fergie T-20, which he bought when he was 11 and which is in daily use yard scraping and moving caravans on the family farm and campsite.

Our Fordson per formed well but wouldn't start at first outside the church; when it did fire up everybody cheered and waved off the new Mr and Mrs Sawle. Both tractors were displayed at the reception and made the day really special. These days they are being used by the family for tractor runs. ∎

A tale of two diesels

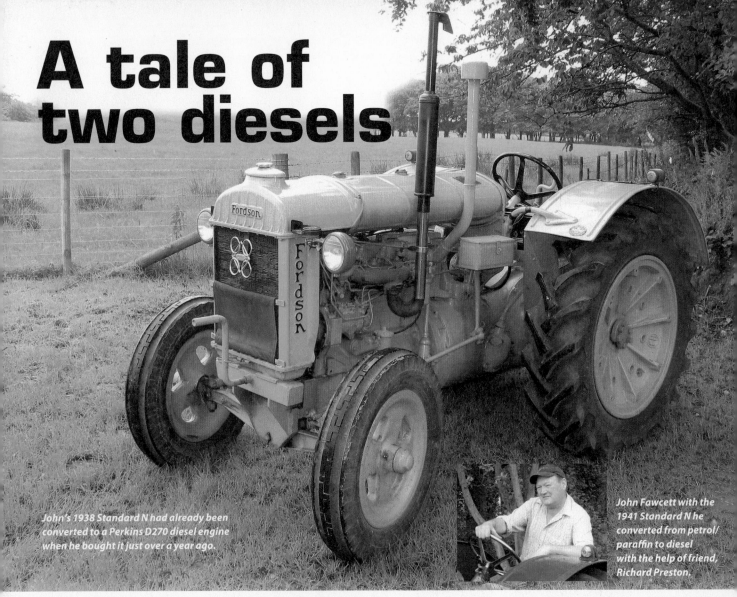

John's 1938 Standard N had already been converted to a Perkins D270 diesel engine when he bought it just over a year ago.

John Fawcett with the 1941 Standard N he converted from petrol/paraffin to diesel with the help of friend, Richard Preston.

How often have you seen someone struggling trying to start their Standard Fordson, especially after a few minutes when the engine has become warm and if it stops, how hard is it to get going again? How nice it would be just to turn a key and watch the Standard N burst into life. Ploughman John Fawcett has found the perfect solution; he is the proud owner of two Standard N tractors, both fitted with diesel engines.

It is believed that the first diesel conversion for the Fordson Standard was a two-cylinder Ailsa Craig 20hp engine rated at 1,200rpm. Roadless Traction Ltd offered this Fordson conversion in about 1937. The Lister Company of Gloucester also fitted one of its diesel-powered engines to an early 1930s Standard N for evaluation purposes, which was a Type CE, a two-cylinder engine developing around 18hp. Perkins Ltd of Peterborough supplied the most popular and wellknown diesel engine conversions. The first Perkins diesel engine fitted to a Standard was a four-cylinder Leopard II developing 34hp. In 1937 Reginald Tildesley, the famous Staffordshire Ford dealer, was one of the first dealers

John saiys that finding a suitable place to fit the battery and electrics can sometimes cause a dilemma with this type of conversion.

Fitted with a Perkins engine, the orange Standard has a hand-made front-end conversion to enable the engine to seat correctly. John used a complete Perkins kit on his blue Standard, which makes for a much simpler job.

The operator platform of the converted Standard N.

to undertake conversions of this nature. Several conversions were undertaken by Ford dealers to suit individual customers' requirements, while several innovative farmers undertook their own conversions in the farm workshop; this often prolonged the working life of a tractor that was quickly becoming outdated.

PERKINS P6 AND L4
Many enthusiasts today convert their tractors, often using Perkins P6 and L4 engines, which now have become more common amongst ploughmen who want a more reliable vintage tractor for ploughing. These tractors could be classed as original working tractors, as

the conversions could have been undertaken during their working lives.

John has been involved in agriculture all his working life, farming 500 acres at Beckermet in the rolling Cumbrian countryside. "About 150 acres of farmland were cultivated for growing cereals with the remaining acreage used to run 500 dairy cattle. Although I ran mainly John Deere machines on the farm, I have always admired Ford and Fordson tractors, so I decided to chose that marque for my collection. I retired from farming three

years ago and although I am not able to do much ploughing these days I am still in touch with everyone through my involvement as a judge at ploughing competitions."

BLUE STANDARD
John's 1941 Standard is presented in the earlier Standard blue livery. John says that he was not struck on green paint, but with his tractor having a Perkins engine fitted, he thought the blue colour would suit his particular tractor better.

Power for the converted Standard comes from a Perkins 4270 1964 fourcylinder engine sourced from a Massey 788

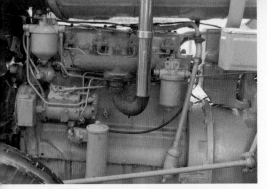

Several companies carried out diesel conversions, the most popular were those supplied by Perkins Ltd of Peterborough.

combine harvester which cost John £150 and with a proper conversion kit, it would have cost £550 fitted. "This conversion was a winter project carried out with the help of my good friend Richard Preston from Newbiggin, who is an agricultural engineer. I decided to do this conversion as a challenge and basically I hadn't got a clue what I was doing," explained John.

Working over the winter of 2006/07, John explained that once he had sourced and sorted all the parts it was quite a straightforward job to undertake. One of the big external jobs which had to be done was to turn the fuel tank around, so the small petrol tank is now at the front and the leakoff pipe from the injectors returns excess diesel into that tank.

126 TEETH

Even though some people choose to fit a stronger E27N clutch on such a conversion, John decided to keep the original clutch system as used with the petrol/paraffin engine. "Once we had ensured that all the measurements were correct, we had no problems with this part of the work," he explained. During the course of the work, John discovered that the starter ring on the flywheel should have 126 teeth where the one fitted to his tractor only had 122. A replacement

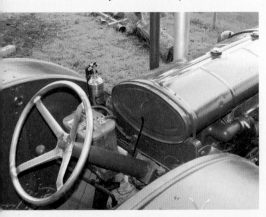

One of the major jobs during the conversion involved turning the fuel tank around to allow excess fuel to be returned to the small tank.

Right: A Perkins 4270 four-cylinder engine, previously fitted to a Massey 780 combine harvester, powers the converted Standard N. An alternator replaced the dynamo which was used on the original petrol/paraffin engine.

starter ring with the correct amount of teeth had to be sourced and fitted.

"One of the most difficult jobs was to find a place to sit the battery and fit all the electrics on the operator platform," explained John. "The electric console I used is also from a Massey 788 combine which I adapted to fit. Talking of electrics, I had to use an alternator and not a dynamo as the alternator was a negative earth.

Overall the electrics were not too bad a job to complete." John says that by using the kit supplied by Perkins for the L4 conversion, minimal work is required to the front end of the tractor to allow the engine to sit correctly as everything matches up and fits perfectly.

The 1941 Standard has a red spot transmission with a high top gear and John says it makes an ideal road-run tractor. "The tractor is slightly heavier with the diesel engine than when fitted with a petrol/paraffin engine, but it is nothing to worry about as the diesel engine has a lot more lugging power.

Best of all, it is a much easier tractor to start and has a good road speed of 15mph, with a little to spare".

ORANGE STANDARD

Another tractor John has is an orange Standard which is also fitted with a diesel engine, although this, too, is a red spot transmission. It is still a good ploughing tractor. "I find the Ransomes RSLD the best plough to use with this particular tractor but these days, the rate of ploughing per hour really depends on

Perkins Ltd of Peterborough was wellknown for its diesel engine conversions. The famous badges are seen sitting proud on many tractor radiators.

the amount of talking I do," he laughed.

"I bought my 1938 orange Standard N just over a year ago. This tractor had already been converted to diesel, having a Perkins D270 engine fitted.

The conversion had been undertaken on the Isle of Wight by a fellow enthusiast, and again, it has the standard clutch fitted."

The orange N is slightly different as it has had a hand-made front-end conversion rather than being fitted with a complete Perkins conversion kit. John went on to say: "Converting the tractors from petrol/paraffin has made them far more economical and more user-friendly. Many Perkins conversions had been undertaken on the farms during the 1950s when the government discontinued the petrol rebate and petrol became too expensive. My Ns are also easy to run and maintain."

CONVERSIONS

Conversions undertaken by Ford dealers all those years ago would have been fairly simple, all the components and parts necessary would have come in a kit and for a trained mechanic it would be a simple job. However, John and Richard had to source various bits and pieces from all over, having to modify and fabricate many other parts which could not be sourced.

Fitting the four-cylinder diesel engine, which has a CAV rotary pump, has increased the power by nearly three times. John says that you have to be very careful with so much power going through the transmission and back end: the power of nearly 60hp at approx 2,000rpm is far greater than the P6 fitted in the E27N rated at 47hp at 1,500rpm.

He adds: "I find the orange diesel N really reliable for ploughing, it keeps going when the going gets tough, and is virtually impossible to stall when in tough going. With the petrol/paraffin engine, when ploughing in tough conditions as would have happened on the farm, the engine would often die down and stall. Believe me, sometimes the petrol/paraffin engine could be extremely difficult to start, but this was sometimes down to the condition of the engine. It was also often hard work ploughing with a petrol/paraffin engine tractor on the farm, but for those who had the engines converted to diesel all those years ago for general farm work, it must have been a godsend." ∎

Adrian Lippiatt from Bristol, with his 1941 Fordson Model N.

A WAR AG FORDSON

Joseph Lewis finds the right man for the tractor

I f ever there was a 'right' owner of a tractor then it is Adrian Lippiatt from Bristol and his Fordson Standard Model N, which was first registered to the Gloucestershire War Agricultural Executive Committee in November 1941.

Adrian takes up the story. "I bought the Model N in 2003 from John Hannan, whose father purchased it in 1949 after a local auction and used it on their farm at Siston near Bristol. The tractor was also used for bringing people and parcels back from Warmley railway station on the outskirts of Bristol.

"My family owned Langton Farm at Siston so our two families' farms were only half a mile apart and I would often see my future Standard."

After 13 years' hard graft the Model N was last taxed in 1962 and stored in a barn until Adrian bought it in 2003.

He said: "During this time we believe the tractor was used on light duties in the yard. This included powering a saw bench and a corn grinder. The Standard was also fitted at one time with an early type of hedgecutter, powered by a separate engine.

"When we looked at the tractor in the barn it was painted a patriotic red and blue colour with traces of green. We also discovered the original engine was fitted with an E27N block in the 1950s. Ford and Fordson dealers Rumsey's of Bristol carried out the work. "I believe my Model N retains the original wings, which I rubbed down. It also has what we understand to be the original rear tyres. I changed the oil rings as the engine was smoking a little bit and fitted a new radiator core.

"I also have my Model N's original log book. This is one of the benefits of it having had one owner for over 60 years and the documentation goes back before this to the War Agricultural Executive Committee.

"On one corner of the log book is 'T28' and I was told this could refer to 'Tractor 28' in the War Ag's fleet of tractors. I would like to know where the tractor was during World War Two and would be grateful for any information.

"Now I take my restored Fordson to local shows and rallies to give me the opportunity to share a tractor which played a local role in the Second World War and has links to my childhood and our next-door farm. In this way, my tractor serves as a catalyst, as many rally goers have enjoyed similar experiences.' ∎

Adrian has the original log book for his Model N which reflects the use by the tractor's first owners, The Gloucestershire War Agricultural Executive Committee. Adrian would like to know where the tractor was during the Second World War.

Brockhouse conversion

It is becoming increasingly rare these days to come across an unusual barn or hedgerow find of such quality and importance as to warrant a full investigation into its heritage. Peter D. Simpson spent an interesting afternoon with Guy and Nick Whitting and a tractor that definitely came into this category.

The Brockhouse conversion to a Fordson Standard N was recently pulled out of the back of a barn after more than 30 years hidden under a pile of accumulated bits and pieces.

During the Second World War, Brockhouse Engineering of Crossens, near Southport, Lancashire, pioneered work in fitting torque converters into agricultural/industrial Fordson Standard tractors. The company was probably best known for its infinitely variable 'Turbo Transmitter' transmission fitted to the David Brown VIG1/462 aircraft-towing tractors that went into production in January 1943. Post-war, Brockhouse produced BMB light tractors, taking over from Shillans Engineering of Banbury after the war.

Commissioned by both the Fleet Air Arm (Royal Navy) and the Air Ministry (Royal Air Force), Brockhouse was asked to develop a tractor suitable for towing and recovery of aircraft as well as hauling munitions and other trailers around war-time airfields both here in the UK and overseas.

At the beginning of World War Two both the RAF (Royal Air Force) and RN (Royal Navy) had been successfully using industrial versions of the Fordson Standard to tow military aircraft. The RN favoured industrial Fordsons (without mudguards) while the RAF usually specified 'Land Utility' models. These tractors served their purpose well until the aircraft became larger and heavier and especially when a plane left the hard runway and became bogged down. Larger aircraft often required more than one tractor to move them, which created a new set of problems. It proved difficult to employ two or three tractors in perfect unison and the consequent snatching and jerking

Guy Whitting.

often caused damage to the aircraft. The clutch on the Standard was difficult to control smoothly. When this was added to the lack of synchronising between the towing tractors, the operation often resulted in damage to the plane's undercarriage.

A direct mechanical drive also led to stalling and wheelslip problems when towing heavy aircraft. The solution was the torque converter; as the tractor throttle was opened, the output torque increased as the drive was taken up smoothly. The engine could not be stalled and a heavy load could be moved from rest without shock or snatch.

The Brockhouse transmission has often been incorrectly referred to as a fluid-flywheel coupling. The company always officially called it a 'Turbo Transmitter' and it was a true torque converter with a two-stage fiveelement unit giving stepless torque multiplication of up to 41/2:1 at stall (ie. when the engine is at full throttle but the output shaft from the torque converter is stationary due to the load imposed on it).

The unit was mounted on a sandwich box between the engine and the gearbox increasing the length of the tractor by 141/2inches. Speeds were infinitely variable between 0 and 30mph; the high top speed thought essential for long distance runways.

It is not known how many conversions of the Fordson were built but it is not thought to be many. It

Above: Initially designed to run solely on petrol, Bert Canton converted the tractor. He fitted a one gallon petrol tank so the tractor could start, the main tank was then used for TVO.

Right: As can be clearly seen, there was not much room for the operator to sit and operate the tractor. The Auto-Mower FR winch carried approximately 100 yards of cable.

appears the majority of the tractors were supplied to the Navy rather than the Air Force but information is rather sketchy. Some confusion has arisen because the Royal Naval Air Stations are customarily referred to as ships. Some thought the Brockhouse Fordsons were used on board ship but this was not the case as they were far too heavy ▶

Nick Whitting returns the tractor to the yard, the Auto-Mower FR Winch can be clearly seen.

and cumbersome for such duties.

The Royal Navy also used these tractors in naval shipyards for hauling motor torpedo boats up slipways and moving heavy wagons of munitions and supplies from warehouses to quaysides. They were also used by the Fleet Air Arm on land-based stations in the Middle East and Far East theatres. Doubtless, many of the tractors were disposed of through the Ministry of Supply surplus auctions. Unsuitable for agricultural work, they might possibly have found some short-lived industrial application or were just broken up for scrap metal.

The Fordson belonging to the Whitting family carries the serial number 977535, which dates it as being built in 1945. Its 51147 RN designation on the tank reveals it to be an ex-Royal Navy tractor. The orange paint is also evidence of its time 'in service' and is more likely vestiges of the 'high visibility orange' favoured by the Fleet Air Arm than Fordson orange, a colour that had been discontinued in 1940

The Whittings' machine is also fitted with an Auto-Mower FR winch. The Auto-Mower Engineering Company of Norton St. Philip near Bath supplied around 200 of the FR winches to the

various armed forces during the war. The winches were used for a variety of purposes from aircraft recovery to timber extraction.

The large rear-mounted drum, with around 100 yards of cable, would have been a useful aid for the recovery of aircraft that had left the runway. The tractor could remain on the hard standing and winch the aircraft off the soft ground.

It is not known where the tractor was originally based or for what type of work it was used. It seems to have done very little, as the Dunlop tyres are original and hardly worn; the

The tractor can do 30mph on the road but it's dangerous to do so. Speed was needed for the long runways that were well over a mile long. Speed is infinitely variable from 0-30mph.

engine is sound and there is no wear in the usual places such as the front axle area. So how did it come to be at Upton Hill in Gloucestershire in the Whitting family's possession?

Guy takes up the story: "My father, Derek Whitting, was a local agricultural contractor. His colleague, Bert Canton, bought the tractor from one of the Ministry of Supplies' Ruddington dispersal sales in about 1950. Bert had just one job in mind for the Fordson – and that was to clear fallen trees with the winch. At the time, the intention was to re-open the Prescott Hill Climb near Cheltenham. This had closed during the war. The plan was to have the course ready for the 1952 season and Bert had been given the job of clearing the many fallen trees and debris from the track after more than 12 years of neglect.

"Bert converted the petrol Fordson to run on vaporising oil by fitting an E27N vaporiser and an extra onegallon tank and using the main tank for TVO. However, the tractor proved to be far from ideal for the task because the transmission overheated at regular intervals and had to be allowed to cool. At the end of 1952 with the job completed, the Fordson was parked up, never to be used again.

"In 1975, while visiting Bert, my father saw the tractor parked behind an old barn where it had stood exposed to the weather for 23 years. He offered to buy it from Bert and a deal was concluded with the exchange of a few pounds and a couple of bottles of whisky. My father had noparticular job in mind for the tractor and he was not interested in collecting. He decided to buy the machine simply because it was there!

"With the tractor back at the farm my brother and I clambered all over it, got it started and ran it for literally minutes before father told us to drive it into the shed and park it up as we had better things to do! The

The front wheel weights approx 2cwt each and were fitted to counterbalance the rear-mounted winch, a heavy duty front axle had also been constructed to give added front weight.

Fordson stayed in the back of the barn and was simply forgotten as it slowly became hidden by wood, tractor parts, engines and other bits and pieces."

There it remained until February, 2007, when a friend was searching the workshop for some engine parts and discovered the tractor beneath all the junk. He persuaded the brothers to pull it out. It took a day to free the tractor from its resting place. The tyres were inflated, the radiator and engine were checked; all the necessary parts were greased or oiled and the plugs were cleaned. A replacement magneto to the same specification as the original was fitted. After an hour of trying, the tractor finally burst into life! Nick drove it out of the shed with the same gusto and enthusiasm as he had driven it into the barn all those years before. The only major problem with the

tractor is that the Fordson's clutch is stuck, so the tractor has to be started in gear, which is possible with the torque converter as the transmission does not take up the drive until the throttle is opened. Apart from a broken front light bracket, a missing battery and the TVO conversion, the tractor is 100 per cent original. From the outset, the brothers decided to leave this important find as it was with its original paint intact. They just gave it a light rub over with a dieselsoaked rag before taking the Fordson on its first outing to the Tractor World Show at Malvern in March 2007, where it created a lot of interest.

Thanks to former Brockhouse Engineering employee John Andrew we have background information on the conversions and we know a lot more about this machine. ∎

Above: The winch is driven from the belt pulley which is also through the torque converter, so the winch starts very slowly and builds up speed as the throttle is opened up.

Right: Officially called a 'turbo transmitter' the torque converter is mounted between the engine and the gearbox increasing the overall length of the tractor by 14½ inches.

The English Standard

Early Ford tractor production was never as precise as that of today's modern machines. Looking at one particular Fordson Standard of the 1930s shows that these machines' specifications could vary from one to another, as Derek Badham explains.

The first true production English Fordson Standard tractors were built at Dagenham from 1933 having in the region of 20 percent more power than its predecessor the Model F, which was in part due to a 100 rpm increase in rated engine speed. When the tractor was first offered it would have been on cast iron front and rear wheels and from 1934 with the option of being fitted on pneumatic tyres.

With production of Fordson tractors at an all time low in the early 1930s, a mere 50 to 60 units a week were being built, the move from Cork to the Dagenham factory saw production start to rise. With the world tractor market beginning to recover and Dagenham in

The early Standard fitted with waterwasher air cleaner is now commonly referred to as the Waterwasher N. In America this type of air cleaner was not liked by farmers as in their cold winters the washer would freeze making the tractor inoperative.

The three forward, one reverse speed transmission was the only transmission available until the introduction of what has become known as the green and red spot transmissions introduced in 1935.

full swing, Fordson tractor production figures increased year on year between 1935 and 1937. Approximately 18,700 units were built during 1937, equating to approximately 360 tractors a week.

This 1937 example which originally worked in Yorkshire and retired to Shropshire has been fully restored by Derek and Margaret Badham. On their search for an MOM to complete the collection of grey Fordsons, Derek went to view an early example but came away with this blue tractor.

On inspection he discovered the tractor engine was stuck as it had not been turned over for a considerable while. Fearing the worst Derek removed the cylinder head and poured diesel into the pots. The diesel was left in for several weeks before he gently tapped the pistons with a block of wood and much to his delight, they freed easily. On further inspection Derek discovered that the engine had been restored not too long previously so after everything was freed it was all put back together and once again to his relief the engine fired up after several short attempts.

After undergoing a full paint job it was decided to leave the original Firestone tyres on all round. "The wheel centres on the Firestone wheels are red where on other manufacturers' versions the colour was more of an orange. Dunlop centres were also red whilst Goodyear centres were yellow, however after 1938 the majority of wheel centres became a uniform colour," explained Derek.

Another unique feature on the Standard of this era was the fitting of a green steering wheel which Derek has replicated well on his particular tractor. "It is firmly believed that the few tractors that appeared with the green steering wheel was down to an individual supplier's design rather than a production design. Several companies had been appointed by the Ford Motor Co to supply parts, but not all parts were of the exact same specification, but were very close, hence tractors appeared with slightly different styled components. The tractor series produced today follows a standard design with the only changes to a particular machine being those specified by the customer," concluded Derek. ■

The steering wheel of the Standard was at a 40 degree angle instead of the almost flat wheel used previously on the Model Fs. Note that this wheel is green; also a new double leaf seat spring replaced the single leaf type of the Model F.

Child of a war hero

A Fordson Major E27N buyer's guide from Andrew Hall

One of the most popular tractors assisting in food production during World War Two was the Fordson model N, also commonly known as the Standard Fordson.

The model N had been around for many years leading up to the war and was already showing its age but, due to wartime restrictions, had to remain in production. Nevertheless, despite shortages of raw materials Ford Motor Company managed to develop a replacement for the N in the shape of the E27N.

The model N had the time-honoured side-valve engine dating back to 1917 when the first model F tractors were introduced.

Attempts were made to develop a new engine for the E27N but this was not ready in time for the first machine to come off the production line on March 19, 1945.

The E27N, or Fordson Major as it was better known, had a similar engine to the N but with certain modifications such as provision for electric starting; it also boasted updated styling with a cast aluminium radiator grille and larger rear wheels to give greater ground clearance.

The main difference between the model N and the new E27N was in the design of the transmission. The worm and wheel final drive of the N was dispensed with and the E27N had revised f inal drive employing spur reduction gears in a new axle casing.

Many people refer to the E27N as a 'stopgap' tractor but in reality the machine enjoyed a seven-year production run with a production total of approximately 230,000 units, many of which found their way into the hands of conversion companies for industrial use in addition to agriculture. The general layout of the E27N set the pattern for subsequent models right up to 1964. Early production models to 1948 were built with a TVO engine but from this date the Perkins P6 diesel engine became available as a production option and also as a conversion for earlier tractors.

The E27N's popularity has increased of late and the following guide should assist a potential buyer to know what to look for when purchasing.

A right-hand view of the engine shows the model N ancestry clearly.

ENGINES: TVO UNIT

The TVO engine could be the Achilles heel of the tractor due to its age and basic design. Many competitors were using overhead valve designs of power unit by the time the E27N was introduced but Ford had not developed an up-to-date unit.

The engine is a four-cylinder in-line unit with side valves, pump assisted thermosyphon cooling, magneto ignition and simple splash-type lubrication. Although the engine is of very simple design it is one of the most demanding engines to rebuild when compared with modern units.

When inspecting with a view to purchase it is a good idea to check all the fluid levels before attempting to start the engine. The lubricating oil should be level with the upper mark on the dip stick. This is important due to the splash nature of the system. The flywheel picks up the oil and delivers it to a tube which carries it forward to the main bearings and timing gears. The bigend caps on the bottom of the connecting rods have dippers attached, which literally dip into the oil and splash it around the other moving parts of the engine. If the engine is worn there may be evidence of heavy vapour breathing from the oil filler cap which is situated on the left-hand side of the cylinder block.

The oil is filtered by a conical filter gauze within the sump, which is accessed and cleaned by removing the sump plate when changing the oil. In normal service the oil should be changed at 60-hour intervals due to the high rate of contamination caused by the use of TVO.

As far as the ignition is concerned, there should be a bright blue spark available from the magneto and this should be timed correctly. When cranking the engine check for correct operation of the impulse coupling, which is designed to hold the magneto still until the engine passes top dead centre, thus preventing kick-back of the engine and providing a better spark at cranking speed.

One safety tip when cranking: keep your thumb the same side as your fingers when holding the starting handle because if the engine does kick back it may dislocate your thumb or break your wrist if you wrap your hand around the handle!

There were two magnetos available in production. The Lucas GJ4, which was carried over from model N days, and the more popular Lucas RF4. Both have provision to adjust the timing of the ignition from the driver's seat.

Another magneto available during the 1950s was the Lucas SR4 which had fixed ▶

The left-hand side shows the usual position of the toolbox when hydraulics are fitted. The other location was under the driver's seat at the rear. Note the oil bath air cleaner.

Steering wheels varied throughout production. Early tractors had the four-spoke wheel, some with Bakelite rim such as this, and some with steel rims which are prone to rust. Later tractors have a three-spoke aluminium wheel.

timing and was a smaller unit distinguishable by the large black distributor cap. Many people have experienced ignition knock with the SR4 magneto, however, due to the fixed timing.

The cooling system contains a large quantity of coolant - approximately 10 gallons - and this should contain adequate anti-freeze to protect from freezing and corrosion. The cylinder block is vulnerable to cracking if insufficient anti-freeze is used, usually on the left-hand side where the casting is flat and only about ¼in thick. Repairs to these can be tricky and may also spoil the look of the block if not carried out neatly,

If a Fordson TVO engine needs rebuilding it may require specialist treatment regarding re-boring the cylinders, remetalling and line boring of the main bearings and bigends due to not having replaceable shells - although big-ends may be adjusted by removing shims. Oversize pistons were originally available in + 0.010in, 0.020in, 0.030in, 0.040in and 0.050in sizes. The fuel system was designed for TVO operation and the original vaporiser used was carried over from the model N with some modifications and a heat shield.

Very early tractors used the model N-type exhaust but later machines have an exhaust pipe with a U-bend. From 1950 a new vaporiser was available and this used a Zenith carburettor and a straight silencer slotting in the top. The air filter is an oil bath-type with a tall extension pipe and flat-topped pre-cleaner.

PERKINS P6 DIESEL UNIT

The Perkins P6 diesel engine provides more power than the original TVO unit. It is a six-cylinder in-line unit providing 45hp at 1500rpm, as opposed to 26.6hp at 1200rpm from the TVO unit.

The P6 is a reliable engine when serviced correctly. Regular oil changes and clean fuel are the secret of its longevity. In early days many farmers didn't realise the importance of clean fuel and many engines suffered as a result. The P6, along with other similar engines, requires the correct oil with high detergency to deal with the carbon.

When viewing a P6-equipped tractor make sure it is cold before starting to demonstrate the starting characteristics. The P6 is equipped with a Ki-gass cold starting aid, which consists of a priming pump and heater coil. It is preferable to use this rather than Easy Start.

Once it is running listen for any knocks or rumbles from the crankcase area, which may indicate worn big-ends or main bearings. Excess fuming from the breather indicates

Belt pulleys were a popular accessory and this tractor sports the earlier compressed fabric type which was carried over from the model N. The later pulley option was cast iron.

The vaporiser on this tractor is the later 'improved' type, but has an aftermarket outlet. The owner is going to fit the correct pattern in due course. This type of vaporiser replaced the original style from May 1950.

Much attention to detail has been paid to this tractor. It has a Smith single lever hydraulic lift. The other option was the Varley, which has two levers, one for the linkage and one for external services. The Smith was the more popular and more reliable of the two. The drawbar is the later more common type also. Earlier drawbars were a thin steel plate fabrication and only appeared on the tractor up to 1946.

worn cylinders, which may accompany poor starting. A good battery is necessary to ensure rapid starting!

Similarly to the TVO unit the P6 is not the easiest of engines to rebuild. Parts availability is an issue and the main bearings and big-ends require line boring when fitted with new shells. The camshaft and injection pump are driven by a triple roller chain, which is also expensive to replace.

The extra power over the TVO unit is very desirable, as is the economy, and a good P6 will give many hours of service if properly maintained.

PERKINS L4 DIESEL UNIT
In addition to the P6 unit, Perkins developed a new four-cylinder diesel engine in the 1950s after production of the E27N had finished. A conversion package was offered and many tractors benefitted from this. The L4 unit had a cubic capacity of 270 cubic inches, as opposed to 288 cubic inches of the P6, and also gear timing drive

instead of the triple roller chain. L4 engines are quite robust but obtaining spares is as difficult as for the P6.

CLUTCH
The clutch on the E27N is a single plate 'wet' type which was supplied by Girling. The term 'wet' relates to the fact it runs in engine oil and uses an appropriate lining material for this. Provided the pedal free play is adjusted properly the clutch is extremely reliable and is not known to give much trouble. Drivers new to the model should note that the pedal is on the righthand side and that takes a little getting used to after driving other tractors.

TRANSMISSION AND BRAKES
The gearbox internals are similar to the earlier model N, albeit with a new input shaft design to suit the clutch. The gearbox is a three-speed (and one reverse) constant mesh type. Ford offered a choice of gear

ratios according to the requirements of the user. Low top gear and high top gear versions were available, together with variations of first and second gear ratios. Tractors with 'red spot' gears have slightly lower first, second and reverse gear ratios whereas 'green spot' tractors have slightly higher first, second and reverse gears. The benefits of red spot are higher drawbar pull for ploughing and similar work. Red spot machines are identified by the letters 'SR' with 4.3 for low top gear whilst green spot tractors have 'STD' with 7.7 for high top gear. This information is on a brass plate under the fuel tank on the left-hand side. If the plate is missing, it is also stamped on the right hand side of the flywheel housing on the gearbox flange. Whether the tractor is high or low top gear, it may have red or green spot ratios.

The gearbox is a strong unit and gives little trouble if lubricated well. The parking brake operates on the reverse gear idler, ▶

With the introduction of the P6-engined Major the bars were turned 90 degrees to allow more air flow. This type of grille was adopted on all post-1949 tractors.

When steel wheels were supplied they followed the same pattern as the old model N, subject to the same dust ring modification as the pneumatic wheel centres.

The first pattern of front wheels has four holes and no dust ring incorporated around the inside of the hub. Compare this shot with the next.

Later pattern wheels have the dust ring behind and smaller holes.

similarly to later Diesel Majors, and is very efficient in action. However, do not drive with it applied as this will damage the plates.

The final drive consists of bull pinion shafts driving spur reduction gears on each axle half-shaft. Independent cableoperated drum brakes work on the bull pinion shafts and are located on the sides of the transmission housing.

One weakness is the failure of the oil seals, allowing oil on to the brakes. This was not overcome until the arrival of the E1A model in late 1951. Modern oil seals should work efficiently in place of the original material.

The hal f-shaf ts were beefed up from 2¼in diameter to 2½in diameter during production to allow for the extra power of the P6 engine.

STEERING AND FRONT AXLE
Two steering boxes were used during the production run. The first version was simply carried over from the model N with worm and sector mechanism but had a longer column.

The steering box was modif ied in 1947 and contained a new worm and nut mechanism. The earlier steering box can be easily identified by the redundant cast bracket (used to hold the air filter on the Model N in place). Later models have a flat cover bolting the steering box to the clutch housing.

Standard agricultural and land utility models have fixed front axles with no width adjustment. Row crop tractors have a threepiece axle which adjusts to suit required widths. All axles are strong and present no specific problems. Wear in king pins, bushes and a track rod pin is not uncommon on well-used machines. These are all replaceable.

TIN WORK
The tin work of the E27N is confined to the rear wings, footplates, fuel tank and early pattern steering wheel. The basic design of the wings did not alter during production, but the reinforcement framework did.

There are three types in existence. The early type consists of a flat steel section curved round to form the frame. This design was only around during 1945. The second design is the more common angle iron frame formed into a vee–shape with a flat brace across the top. The final designs from late 1948 consist of two upright box sections spot-welded together.

All styles are susceptible to rust, the earlier type in the sheet metal and the later in the box sections too. Replacement wings are available from various sources.

Footplates did not change during manufacture and are also vulnerable to rust. Fuel tanks suffer from rust and often rust under the f ixing straps. Internal

Rear wheels fitted to earlier tractors were 9.00-36 rims with ten lugs, as shown here. Later tractors benefited from the fitment of 11.00-36 rims which have eight lugs. Traction was greatly improved with the wider tyres.

Die-cast aluminium grilles were fragile. This is the earlier pattern with wide bars - in my opinion the nicer grille.

corrosion also occurs, particularly where the starting tank joins the main tank inside. When this occurs the starting petrol can leak through to the TVO and vice-versa, thus causing difficult starting and/or poor running.

The early four-spoke steering wheel suffers corrosion around the rim. The rims are available to weld on to the spokes. Later steering wheels are made of cast aluminium and have three spokes.

The radiator grille is die-cast in aluminium and is vulnerable to damage. Two versions of the grille were available during production: the early pattern had wide bars and the latter had the bars turned 90 degrees, allowing more air flow. The earlier grille is the more attractive of the two, but until recently only reproduction grilles of the later style were available.

WHEELS

Early tractors, known as standard agricultural, had steel wheels and no independent brakes. The front wheels were similar to the model N with five holes, whilst the rear wheels had pressed centres with steel rims and removable spade lugs.

Land utility and row crop machines used pneumatic tyres. Pneumatic front wheels also followed model N pattern with fourhole cast centres. In 1949 a dust ring was added to the front wheel castings to protect the bearings from mud etc. This applied to both steel and pneumatic wheels. The early pneumatic rear wheels were narrow at 9in-wide and have ten lugs to attach the centres. These were superseded by wider 11in-wide wheels to improve traction and these have eight lugs.

ACCESSORIES

I have included some items as accessories in this section that would normally be classed as standard on many other tractors because many E27Ns were supplied as basic tractors with just a drawbar as standard.
Power take-off A pto of 1 3/8in diameter was available and fitted to many E27Ns. This was driven from the bottom of the gearbox and runs through the rear axle housing.

BELT PULLEY

The belt pulley was fitted to the right-hand side of the clutch housing and was available in compressed fabric or, more commonly, cast iron. Most tractors were fitted with the belt pulley as power from this was more commonly required during the 1940s and early 1950s.

HYDRAULIC LIFTS

When the E27N was introduced three-point linkage was in its infancy and most early tractors were supplied without a lift. When the lift became more readily available two designs were available. Firstly the Smith lift, which was distinguished by the large J-shaped aluminium control lever, and secondly the Varley lift, which had two levers, one for the main lift and a second

This is a basic TVO E27N with no hydraulics, but electric starting and a lighting kit fitted.

Another TVO version. This one has the Smith-type lift fitted and toolbox on the left-hand side of the engine.

for external hydraulic services. Both types are driven from the top of the gearbox and different sets of gears are required for low or high top gear tractors, so anybody considering retro-fitting must ensure they have the correct drive gears.

The lifts were simply up or down with no draft control, as this was covered by Ferguson patents at the time. The systems have their own oil supply and this must be maintained at the correct level for good performance.

The Smith version is the more common of the two and is said to be more reliable than the Varley. Category two linkage is common to both units when fitted.

Wheel weights Cast iron wheel weights were available and fitted to the centres of the rear wheels. Three weights per side could be fitted, each of 100lbs.

ELECTRICAL ACCESSORIES

Starting and lighting were available, but early tractors didn't have a starter ring on the engine flywheel. When so fitted the 12 volt battery is located on a cast bracket bolted to the upper dashboard and headlamps are attached to cast iron arms and one rear lamp is attached to the rear axle housing.

Two control boxes were available, the earlier one being kidney shaped and the later type rectangular, both of which are bolted to the steering column. Other smaller accessories included a bulb horn and a rear ▶

This fully-equipped Perkins P6 version has the rear wheel weights, which were one of the optional extras.

In 1953 Perkins introduced the L4 engine as a conversion, and this is an example of such a machine. The conversion used the original pattern of exhaust pipe from the early TVO vaporiser, albeit on the left-hand side. Also, the fuel tank was turned the opposite way round.

price. Values of Perkins engined models have increased greatly, with prices starting from £4,000.

CONCLUSION

Although the tractor was considered a stopgap machine for Ford, it certainly made a big impression on the tractor market in its time and contributed greatly to mechanising farms that had seen little before.

The TVO engine is a bit thirsty for regular use and can be temperamental, too. Diesel models are more economical but care must be taken in selecting good ones, as they are expensive to repair.

Overall they are fun to own and operate in preservation.

* Many thanks to Melvin Broughton of Hadlow, Kent, for the views of the restored example. ∎

E27N SPECIFICATIONS	
TVO engine	
Fuel	Petrol/ Tractor Vaporising Oil
Number of cylinders	Four
Capacity	4380cc
Valve configuration	Side valves
Bore/stroke	4⅛in/5in
Horsepower	26.7 @ 1200rpm
Perkins P6 Engine	
Fuel	Diesel
Number of cylinders	Six
Capacity	288 cubic inches - 4.7 litres
Valve configuration	Overhead valve
Bore/stroke	3½in/5in
Horsepower	45 @ 1500rpm
Perkins L4 Engine	
Fuel	Diesel
Number of cylinders	Four
Capacity	270 cubic inches - 4.47 Litres
Valve configuration	Overhead valves
Bore/stroke	4¼in/4¾in
Horsepower	45 @ 1500rpm
Transmission	
Gears	Three forward/ one reverse
Red spot type	Low 1st and 2nd ratios
Green spot type	Higher 1st and 2nd ratios
4.3 transmission	Low top gear
7.7 transmission	High top gear

view mirror, although not many tractors will still have these fitted today.

SPARES AVAILABILITY

Availability of spares is variable, according to which engine option is fitted. Whichever engine you have, if it requires any significant overhauling it is best left to the variety of specialists who provide the necessary machining facilities.

Beyond the engine many parts are the same as the later E1A models, particularly axle and steering components. Most parts likely to be required are available from the following suppliers/specialists;

Old Twenty Parts Company, tel: 01332 792698 for general spares

Cox & Turner, tel: 01202 823322 for specialist engine repairs and spares (TVO) engine.

Cotwold Vintage Tractors, tel: 01386 841983 for tin work, new and used parts.

Paul Gardner Engineering, tel: 01524 791507 for specialist re-metalling, line boring and diesel injection equipment servicing.

PRICES

After a period of relatively stable values the E27N models have increased steadily in recent times. Expect to pay £750 to £1,000 for a basic TVO tractor in running order, but in need of restoration. TVO models in good running order and requiring little work can fetch between £2,000 and £2,500. The more accessories the tractor possesses will also be reflected in the asking

John Allsop supplied this photograph of his 1947 Fordson E27N tvo land-utility Major, which is seen at Heage Windmill near Belper, Derbyshire.

He has owned the tractor since 1981 and in 2004 finished a three-year back-to-bare-metal restoration with new rear wings, new front tyres and second-hand radiator.

Born again

David's tractor is a lovely example of the marque.

Twenty years after it was vandalised and abandoned an E27N is brought back to life. Bob Weir reports

When the wind whistles over Scotland's Lammermuir Hills it's enough to give anyone the shivers, but one sight of David Ritchie's pristine E27N Perkins diesel put the smile back on my face.

The Ritchie family are well known around East Lothian and have farmed on the outskirts of Haddington for over a century. They have 120 acres, with the majority given over to barley and the rest rented out to grow potatoes.

David also finds time to do volunteer work at nearby Prestongrange Industrial Museum, one of the most important heritage sites in Scotland.

So that's the family - now to introduce the E27N, the last in the line of the legendary Fordson N series, which can trace its roots all the way back to the late-1920s.

By the end of the Second World War, the N's design had started to look dated and in an ideal world the Ford management at Dagenham would have preferred to produce a brand-new tractor, or build the more modern Ford-Ferguson.

Unfortunately, in the difficult economic conditions that prevailed following the end of hostilities, they had little room for manoeuvre and a further upgrade to the veteran Model N was the only viable option.

Despite Fordson's excellent reputation with British farmers, the petrol E27N only met with modest success. The venerable 27hp engine was now being pushed to its limits, although it was still capable of performing as a three-plough tractor, thanks to the introduction of the new bevel-drive rear axle.

The overall weight had risen to a hefty 4,000lbs, a substantial increase on the original design. In its new high-compression format, the service life of the 267ci/1,200rpm engine was also limited. To make matters worse overhauls were complicated by the lack of cylinder sleeves, which meant worn-out units had to be re-bored.

Fortunately, a solution was at hand.

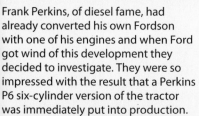

The legendary Perkins P6, developed by *Frank Perkins and Charles Chapman, provides the power for David Ritchie's fabulous Fordson E27N.*

separate control for external services, or a single lever Smith unit. Both systems were self-contained bolt-on affairs, driven by a shaft from the engine's gearbox.

In true Fordson fashion, the tractor was also offered with a large range of approved accessories from the Ford factory in Warwickshire. These included Elite two and three-furrow trail ploughs, cultivators and ridgers. Ransomes also chipped in with a range of tillage implements and the Martin Cultivator Company offered a mid-mounted tool bar. Other suppliers included Compton loaders, Robot vegetable planters, Bamford mowers, Dening saw benches and Allman powder dusters.

Unlike the petrol version, the diesel E27N was a great success and 23,000 were built before production ended in 1952. This figure doesn't include the large number of petrol models that were eventually converted to diesel using either the P6 or P4 (four-cylinder) engines.

David's tractor was built in 1948 and started life using petrol/paraffin. The Fordson was equipped with a hydraulic lift but lacked a power take-off unit (pto). It is thought to have been used for row crop work, and eventually had its mudguards removed when it was fitted with a Horndraulic loader.

"Once the farm acquired one of the new diesel Majors, the workload of the E27N ▶

well on its way to becoming market leader.

The diesel E27N was recognisable by the 'four-rings' Perkins badge at the front of the tractor. It still retained the original petrol version's clutch and transmission, although the rear axle was strengthened to cope with the extra weight. A hydraulic implement lift was optional with a choice of either a twin-lever Varley system with

Frank Perkins, of diesel fame, had already converted his own Fordson with one of his engines and when Ford got wind of this development they decided to investigate. They were so impressed with the result that a Perkins P6 six-cylinder version of the tractor was immediately put into production.

Although it weighed 500lb (227kg) more than the petrol model, the introduction of the P6 transformed the E27N, producing an impressive 45hp at 1,500rpm. More significantly, it finally proved to the farming community that diesel engines were a viable alternative and here to stay.

Frank Perkins was born in Peterborough on February 20, 1889. His father and grandfather had run the engineering firm Barford and Perkins for several years, manufacturing agricultural machinery and road rollers. But it was while he was

David's tractor has both a hydraulic three-point linkage and a pto unit.

The manufacturer's plate fitted to the manifold of the Perkins six-cylinder unit.

gradually tapered off," says David, who is also a self-taught engineer. The tractor did a stint as dung spreader before it was used to drive an irrigation pump with the help of a pto kit supplied by the local Ford agents. This continued into the early-1960s, when it was vandalised and had to be laid up.

David recalls: "The tractor was more or less abandoned, although I used to tinker around with it when I had the spare time."

He eventually decided to dismantle it altogether, scrapping the engine and storing the other parts, and it was not until he spotted some restored E27Ns at shows some 20 years later during the mid-Eighties that his Fordson's fortunes took a turn for the better.

He admits to never having been a big fan of petrol/paraffin tractors and found the idea of a diesel restoration far more appealing. Then, just by chance, he was doing some contract work at nearby East Fortune when he came across a P6 diesel

fitted to an old County crawler. He decided, on the spur of the moment, to buy the crawler and use the engine in SS 6949.

According to David, this particular P6 probably started life in a lorry. For evidence he points to the engine's exhauster that is positioned to create a vacuum for the brakes of a four-wheeled vehicle.

Once he had hunted around for a few spare parts, it was relatively straightforward to put the E27N back together again. Now the tractor performs as good as new, and David takes it to the occasional show.

In addition to the Fordson, David also owns a TEF 'little grey Fergie' that he swapped in the late Seventies for one of his motor cars. When he bought the tractor it had been painted green, but it has since been restored to the more familiar grey colour scheme. Apart from the new coat of paint no restoration work was carried out, and its condition is pretty much as it was when it left the factory. The TEF-

20 runs smoothly and still does the occasional spot of work around the farm.

Over the years David has also accumulated several other tractors for what he fondly calls 'pending' restoration. The Massey Fergusons 35, 65 and 135 are mostly in bits and the same applies to the Major E1A. I also spotted an IH TD6 and 125 loading shovel. Finally there are the MF models 590, 595 and 1080 that at some point in their careers have all served as the farm's resident tractors. His current workhorse is a Case International 5130.

Thanks to the support of his wife Christine, David has a number of other irons in the fire. Apart from a growing collection of classic lorries, there is also his volunteer work at the Prestongrange Industrial Heritage Museum.

Situated on the Firth of Forth the site is a unique reminder of Scotland's past, and can boast several rare exhibits. These include a Hoffman kiln, and the only remaining Cornish Beam Engine in Scotland.

"Finding the time to fit everything in is probably the biggest headache," David explains with a rueful smile. And, with a long queue of tractors waiting in the yard for restoration, that situation doesn't look like changing.

*Further information: Prestongrange Museum, Morrison's Haven, Prestonpans, East Lothian. Tel: 0131 653 2904 or visit the website: www.prestongrange.org ∎

A Fordson Major E1A and MF 35 await restoration.

The tale of an Orkney E27N

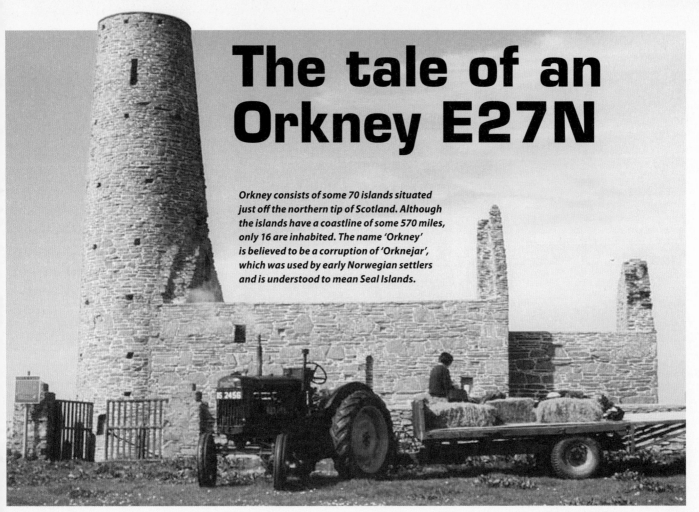

Orkney consists of some 70 islands situated just off the northern tip of Scotland. Although the islands have a coastline of some 570 miles, only 16 are inhabited. The name 'Orkney' is believed to be a corruption of 'Orknejar', which was used by early Norwegian settlers and is understood to mean Seal Islands.

Leslie Alexander lives in Kirkwall, the capital of Orkney; he shares the history of his Fordson E27N which began its working life with the Alexander family on the islands and has now returned to his care.

I n early 1947 a young man called Douglas Alexander was living and working on the family farm of Kirbist on the small island of Egilsay in the Orkney Islands with his brother and father. Although the family was still using a horse for cultivating part of the land, a 1941 Fordson Standard N undertook the rest of the work on the 250-acre farm.

Douglas was to be married in May and was to leave Kirbist to begin farming the nearby 200 acres of Onziebust. It had been decided that a further tractor would be needed to work the extra acreage. An order for an E27N Major Basic Land Utility model was placed with the local agricultural merchants in Kirkwall, J & W Tait Ltd. and the tractor duly arrived on 26 April 1947 bearing registration number BS 2456.

Leslie takes up the story: "This would have been quite an event at the time because there were very few tractors on the island, and the Major was a big impressive machine. My uncle, a small boy at the time, remembers well all the children at the school rushing to the roadside to see this big dark blue tractor with bright orange wheels drive past."

Douglas Alexander in the mid-1950s – the shield covering the engine was there to protect the magneto from salt water when going down Egilsay pier.

ONLY MEANS OF TRANSPORT

In addition to carrying out the work on the farm, the Major was the only means of transport for the family so a full electrical kit was fitted to make starting easier, as well as ensuring lights to help the driver see the road at night. Several years later a hydraulic lift and a Horndraulic loader were fitted to make the tractor more versatile. In 1956 an International B250 was bought thereby reducing the Major's workload. During 1959 an International B275 was purchased and the E27N was relegated to loader work on both farms. Each year the Major was dragged out of the corner of the old stone shed where it sat, fired up and ▶

Above and below: Loading dung at Onziebust, mid-1950s.

Out of the shed for the first time.

was put to use clearing the muck middens.

By 1978, time and many years of lying covered in dung had taken its toll on the tractor; the steering was so worn it was almost impossible to steer and the Major was retired and parked up in the field after 31 years of faithful service. Another International B250 fitted with a loader was bought as the replacement.

DAMP SALT ISLAND AIR

Usually when this happens, especially in the Orkney islands with the damp salt air, the tractor would quickly rot and be reduced to scrap in a very short time. For some reason Douglas decided to advertise the Major for sale at £60 in the local paper. Maybe he had a fondness for her after all the years of service and didn't want to see her decay beyond repair.

There was no real interest in the vintage tractor scene in Orkney at that time, but a man named Dudley Peck, who worked in the Agricultural College in Kirkwall, saw the advert and thought the Major would be a good tractor for him to restore. A deal was struck and BS 2456 was loaded onto the boat and left Egilsay for the first time in 31 years.

The following year, Dudley spent his spare time cleaning and painting. New mudguards were fitted and a brand-new grille replaced the original which had been damaged, probably by hitting trailers when on loader work.

THE SEARCH BEGINS

"In early 1995 I attended a farm sale where an E27N was up for auction. I began to think that I would like to get hold of an old Major and it was then I decided to

try to find BS 2456," explained Leslie.

"I didn't think this would be too hard, all I had to do would be to telephone Mr. Peck and see if he would sell. But things are never that easy, are they? Mr. Peck had moved to Elgin in the 1980s, then to the Isle of Man and when I finally contacted him he explained that he had sold the Major to a coal merchant somewhere in the North East of Scotland, around Buckie he thought."

Leslie believed his chances of finding the Major were very slim, but eventually spoke to a coal merchant in Buckie called Charlie Hepburn who confirmed that he owned an old Major with the registration number BS 2456, which he would consider selling. Fortunately, Leslie's brother-in-law, Harvey Sutherland lived in Aberdeen and offered to go and look at the tractor to check its condition. A deal was struck and Harvey who

Taking in sheaves – a traditional scene on one of the Orkney islands.

A successful working day when the E27N was put through its paces.

owned a beaver-tailed lorry transported the Major to the docks at Aberdeen ready to be shipped to Orkney. On 15 April 1995 BS 2456 arrived back on the Kirkwall pier. Although the tractor had been standing outside for several years, once the fuel tank had been cleaned and the plugs and magneto dried out, the engine fired up.

RETURN TO THE ORKNEYS

Over the next five years Leslie entered several ploughing matches and vintage rallies but, as anyone who has used an E27N will know, the machine can be very temperamental.

"At home when no one was about, the Major usually went quite well but when there was an audience, such as at a working day or vintage rally, you could be sure there would be a misfire or, worse still, no life at all," Leslie recalled. "As anyone else who has been in the same predicament will know, there is always an expert on the field who seems to know better than you what to do. In situations like this, one must cheerfully accept all advice given, albeit through gritted teeth.

"Well, after one particularly bad working day when nothing seemed to fix the misfire, the Major was taken home in disgust, put in the back of the shed and left for four months untouched. Then, on the day of a vintage rally I went to the shed, put in some petrol, and away she went as smooth as you like, not a misfire to be heard. It was clear her behaviour was not acceptable and things were going to have to change."

A friend had fitted a Perkins 4.270 engine to a Standard Fordson using an L4 conversion kit so Leslie decided that was the way to go. Perkins 4.270 engines had been fitted in combines so were relatively easy to locate, but the conversion kit was not so easy to find, especially on remote islands such as

the Orkneys. A sump from a scrap E27N was located but the front casting and flywheel were missing. However, contact was made with a retired employee of Perkins, who very kindly obtained copies of the engineering drawings of the front casting. Then a very good friend, Vincent Sinclair, set to work with some steel and a welder and made an exact copy of the front casting.

The flywheel also proved to be very difficult to find even though adverts were placed in various tractor magazines and contacts all over the country were telephoned. Eventually an L4 was found at Huntly, near Aberdeen, and with the help of Harvey, yet again, Leslie now had all the parts to complete the conversion.

TO THE WORKSHOP

In October 2001 the Major was taken in the workshop and the paraffin engine removed. With the help of father-in-law Billy Skea, the conversion work was carried out and in spring 2002 the Major emerged in all its refined glory.

Leslie concluded: "Now some may say this has spoiled the originality of the Major, but since the conversion it has become a very usable tractor, which I use at every opportunity and I'm sure Douglas Alexander, its first owner, would have approved. Anyway, I could always put the paraffin engine back in, but somehow I don't think that will ever happen." ■

Loading at Mr. Hepburn's with Billy Skea at the wheel and Harvey Sutherland on the winch controls.

Down at the carnival

For so many years there were a good circuit of carnivals in the south coast that lasted in the traditional sense until the 80's. The parade through the high street or promenade was the high point, which normally ended up at Andrews Fairground Amusements who followed such events around each season in Kent and East Sussex. They started out from their Tunbridge Wells winter quarters in March and returned in late November, after the bonfire parade season had finished, but Teddy Andrews fair is just a distant memory now. The annual carnival would have seen judging for the best float, trade stand and of course the delightful carnival queen and her lovely attendants who every teenage boy wanted to kiss if they had half the chance! Many of the motor trade supported such events with vigour, particularly in the post war austerity era and well beyond.

Besides J Hollingsworth there would also be Caffyns the 'new' Nuffield agent. Even then Caffyns were known for their elaborate carnival stands, but Hollingsworth were just not going to be out done with this incredible adaption of one of their Land Utility petrol paraffin E27Ns. What an incredible amount of dedicated hard work has gone into it, just look at the picture closely. The tractor carries the industrial downswept exhaust and a whole manner of modifications that had made 'Featherbed Farming' something very special indeed. The company would have been seen from Rye to Battle, Hastings, Bexhill and nearly to Brighton where the burgeoning Endeavour Motors were the Ford 'kings'. Those were the days when you dressed up in your best and the excitement of the event was certainly enjoyed by all the family and by holiday makers alike. Do you have any pictures like this? The editor would be delighted to print them in Ford and Fordson Tractors please do get in touch, the more the merrier we say.

NGSWORTH ᴸᵗᵈ.

XXX

GENTS
OUTFITTERS

NE

TAILORING

Wilfred Embery

ARMING

Fordson

Fordson

O58 DY

A Period Setting

Some people collect tractors for working purposes, whilst others restore them to a high standard to exhibit. Not Jeremy French – he has restored his Fordson Major E27N for the two reasons mentioned, but also to replicate the atmosphere of farming in post-war years.

Jeremy, a young engineer who lives near Maldon in Essex, has a strong affinity with the country's agricultural and rural heritage and believes that restoring and preserving tractors and machines should be themed sympathetically to a certain era.

The tractors and machines that Jeremy has restored are not necessarily to factory specification but restored to a high standard as the tractor would have been on the farm. 'Quite often farmers or operators would slightly modify their tractors to suit individual requirements as well as for specific operations. These changes and modifications have shown through in my restorations,' explained Jeremy.

One case in point is the D Ward of Long Melford tumbril cart that was originally a horse-drawn cart which has been adapted to fit behind a tractor. Built pre-war, the trailer was converted after 1945 being fitted with a drawbar and rubber tyres. The wheels complete with tyres came from an ex-army vehicle which were Pirelli 10.50x16s mounted on split rims.

THE TUMBRIL CART

Ward established an iron foundry in Long Melford, Essex in 1843, becoming an important business in the village, employing 63 men and four boys in 1881. There are many examples of Ward's work in the village and surrounding areas, with its tumbril cart being just one example of the company's later work.

'The tumbril cart was often used as a milk cart; the milk was put into churns and taken to the local dairy. The two-wheel cart was also used for transporting produce to and from the local market and railway station,' explained Jeremy, who went on to say: 'It was an essential vehicle for the farmer, especially when inspecting and feeding the livestock out in the fields or when housed in barns away from the main farmstead, also for travelling out to the harvesting and haymaking fields.'

Surprisingly this type of open cart that was designed for farm and general transport use was once used to carry condemned prisoners to their place of execution, as during the French Revolution.

This two-wheeled farmer's cart was mostly used for hauling farmyard manure out to the fields from the stockyard, where it was tilted to discharge its load. When horses pulled this type of cart to the fields the only way of discharging its load was by releasing a catch at the front of the trailer, when the load tipped and discharged itself by counterbalance weight. The Waggoner then pulled the tipped body back down

and locked it in transport position again.

As a point to note, a cart has two wheels, a waggon has four wheels (road waggons have two 'g's in their name, railway wagons only have one), both are used as general purpose vehicles mainly for the transportation of goods. On early horse-drawn agricultural vehicles the driver either walked alongside or rode one of the horses in the team, and this man became known as the Waggoner.

When Jeremy purchased the trailer which was in a fairly sorry state he had to replace a lot of the woodwork on the body carefully trying to replicate the original style, with much of the wooden chassis being replaced by steel, following on with a full paint job to the pre-war style.

One of the major problems Jeremy encountered was removing the tyres from the rims as they had rusted on. 'I came up with the idea which sounded a bit over the top at the time which was to drive the farm's Ford 4000 over the tyre to break the bead, which it successfully did,' explained Jeremy who concluded:

'The cart was fitted with a pair of ex-army run flats that had the canvas showing through and I knew these would have to be replaced. The 10.50x16s that were on it when I bought it did look a little out of scale and replacements were not easily obtainable. As luck would have it, an enquiry led me to a pair of suitable Michelin 9.00x16 tyres from an ex-army field ambulance. These not only looked the part but ▶

The tumbril cart was often used to carry condemned prisoners to their place of execution, as during the French Revolution. Here it is in the more sedately agricultural mode.

had a narrow escape from the tyre cutter as they were destined for an off-road vehicle. Now they sit nicely on my cart.'

Once the cart was completed Jeremy thought it should look the part and required a period load. 'What the load was going to be caused me somewhat of a dilemma. Again the post-war era had to be considered, so I opted for a choice of either using milk churns or a load of filled sacks replicating grain sacks,' said Jeremy.

Here lay a problem, Jeremy wanted to find half a dozen hessian sacks from the 1950s-60s period. Looking through various local auction listings he noticed that one auction had listed several grain sacks of the type he wanted. Off he went and successfully bid on the said items. To his dismay there weren't just a few sacks, but two pallets full of bundles of sacks all in perfect, clean, rodent damage free condition.

THE TRACTOR

The Fordson Major, which Jeremy has owned since 1994, is from late 1951. With all the possible extras it could have had fitted at the time which included lights, horn, hydraulics, high-speed gear box and the electric starting are essential Jeremy. It is far better than trying to start it with the handle.

Jeremy explained: 'The E27N tractor was found in an ex-council lock up garage partially stripped and in several boxes, the wings had long since been lost in a fire. It took some time to sort through all the bits just to try and work out what was and wasn't there. The parts I needed were obtained from a range of sources, rallies, auctions and a donor tractor that had spent its life

It might take some finding, but to maintain a period theme it is worth taking a little time to locate the correct items.

in a boat yard. The salt water had taken its toll on this sorry-looking machine, but several parts including the major castings and the starter for the conversion to electric starting were in reasonable condition.'

The Major E27N had always been a favourite of Jeremy's and he was extremely pleased with his finished project. 'I was asked in early 2008 if I would take my tractor to the Museum of Power which

was planning an event to celebrate the Land Army Centenary, I decided I would have to make some sort of display fitting to the period and the museum.'

The Museum of Power, set in seven acres of grounds and housed in the Steam Pumping Station at Langford in Essex, exhibits and demonstrates working examples of power sources of all types and chronicles the major roles that they have played in history. The museum aims to provide an entertaining and educational environment in which to explore our use of power and presents fascinating working examples of machinery, equipment and tools which have been used to develop the industrial and social conditions we enjoy today.

It was for this particular event that Jeremy pulled out all the stops and displayed his tractor, trailer and load plus several other items including a board showing the various tools used to work on the Fordson tractors. There was also a small display of hand tools and other agricultural-related bygones that would have been seen around the farm and used by the Land Army girls during the war.

'A Shire horse and a selection of period Land Army clothing were brought along by a friend and together the display attracted a lot of interest. There were comments from various people saying how much better the complete period display looked; it had more of a meaning than just a tractor standing on its own would have done,' commented Jeremy.

Jeremy's collection of Fordson tractors starts with models that preceded the E27N. There are several fully-restored Standard Ns in the collection, all with a different story to tell. ∎

Electric starting is a must says Jeremy; it is far easier than trying to start the tractor with the handle.

Rare industrial E27N

Ryan Baker uncovers a rather unusual
Ford E27N with a very interesting history

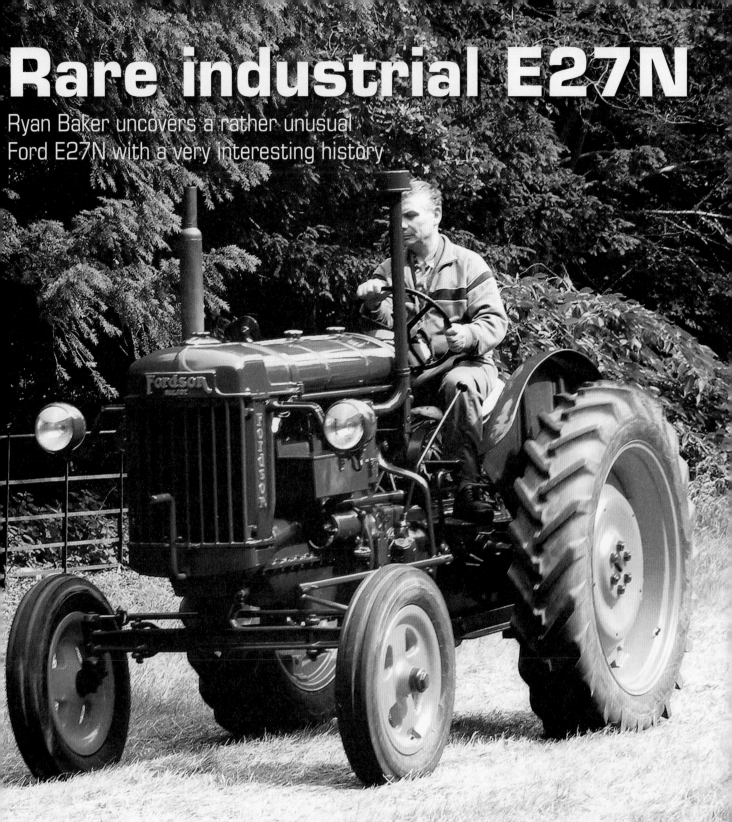

t a distance the tractor in question may look like an 'ordinary' E27N. However, this old girl has her brake drums on the outside of her axle trumpets, as opposed to the inner bull pinions as was fitted on all other Fordson Major tractors. The brakes are operated by just one foot pedal whereas the standard brakes were operated by two brake pedals (one for each side). It was not fitted with hydraulics, only a drawbar for towing purposes. Electrics were fitted which included headlights and starting facilities.

FORD FACTORY WORKHORSE
The tractor started its life in the Ford factory in Dagenham in 1946 and was used for pulling sledges transporting oil barrels and other equipment, around the factory. Here the tractor played an important part on the production line in the making of new tractors.

During this time whilst working in the factory, the tractor ran on petrol only. However, when its life was finished at the factory, before selling the tractor on, Ford converted it to enable it to run on paraffin. (It was often the case that formally petrol powered industrial E27Ns were

converted during their working lives to run on diesel fuel by fitting the Perkins P6 45 h.p. engine.) When in the 1950's the new improved manifold became available, it was fitted with one of these.

The tractor, which is owned by Derrick Leech was treated to a full restoration about three years ago. This was a complete renovation, both mechanically and cosmetically. Derrick's brother Geoff carried out the restoration work. The tractor, now in superb condition, is used regularly on Road Runs by both Derrick and Geoff. ∎

E27N restoration

Keith Morton and his wife Jackie from the Vale of Belvoir Machinery Group have been busy restoring their Fordson E27N, as Keith explains

We bought the tractor in august 2008 and soon found that she had been standing outside for some time. As the engine was running quite nicely when we got her we decided to concentrate on other areas for the restoration. The wings were taken off and sand blasted to see what was under the old paint, a few hours work was needed with the welder to tidy up the metal work.

The rear wheel rims were in a poor state and needed many hours work to get them back to how they look now. Initially they were sand blasted at a local farm. We then decided to re-weld the centre lugs to strengthen them, this was a job done by my father-in-law. A new seat and steering wheel were purchased as the originals were well beyond repair and far easier to replace. We spent many hours rubbing down the old paint work. When it came to the fuel tank this was removed, dents were knocked out and then it was prepared for spraying.

The main body of the tractor was wire brushed down to remove most of the rust - this was probably the hardest part of the restoration as we had 60 years of rust to deal with. Once we were happy we had done enough here a rust inhibitor was sprayed on and left to dry for a week. Red under coat was sprayed and left to dry for a further week followed by a grey under coat. We sprayed the blue top coat on a fine Sunday morning in August, with the wife doing the paint mixing and me spraying! The small parts were sprayed at home, the fuel tank, seat and front wheels were cleaned off and sprayed Fordson blue. The front wheels, which had red rather than orange paint on them were sprayed Fordson orange then new inner tubes and tires were fitted along with new wheel bearings.

THE REBUILD

Within another couple of weeks we had sourced a new radiator and fuel tap – then came the hard job of putting it all back together! The brakes were relined and fitted back on, followed by the foot plates, the wings, front grill, new radiator and the fuel tank. By this stage she was starting to look like a tractor again. We were left with just a few little bits left like changing the oil, putting fuel in the tank... and then we were off!

It took us more than six months to get a registration number before we could order new number plates; this is something to consider early on if you plan to take your tractor on the road and don't really want to be held up waiting for paperwork. Another tip - we found keeping a list of all of the jobs to be done and ticking them off as they were completed very useful. It makes you realise how much you have done and you know exactly what is left to finish the job off. ■

The tractor before the restoration started

Resting on jacks, partially stripped down with all of the wheels removed

A common condition with steering wheels on older tractors – but new replacements are not expensive

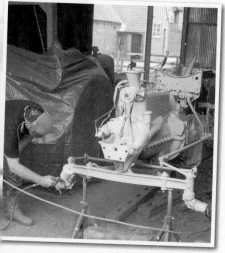

Keith gives the tractor a coat of grey undercoat, on top of the rust inhibitor and red primer

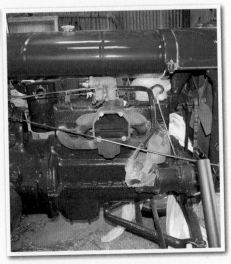

The exhaust hot boxes were sourced from Cotswold tractors

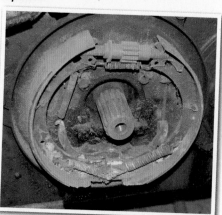

The brake drum cover here was pulled off to find the brake shoes in poor condition, the parts were taken off and cleaned. The back plate was removed, shot blasted and re-sprayed. New springs, liners and brake cables were sourced from Old 20 Parts

One of the rear wheels before being sandblasted. The lugs were also re-welded to strengthen them

With Old Twenty Fordson blue and Old Twenty Fordson orange top coat painted, the tractor is beginning to take shape again

Rear wheels back on, radiator and steering wheel fitted, just a few finishing touches and she's finished

---

A big thank you to Nick at Old Twenty Parts, who has helped us a lot with paint, oils and many other things needed for our restoration

SUPPLIERS

Paints	Old 20 Parts	Wheel bearings	Old 20 Parts	Exhaust hot box	xCotswold Tractors
Fan belt	Old 20 Parts	Brake linings	Old 20 Parts	Steering wheel	Cotswold Tractors
Radiator	Old 20 Parts	Brake rivets	Old 20 Parts	Seat	Boyt Brothers
Fuel tap	Old 20 Parts	Draw bar pins	Old 20 Parts	Front grill	Boyt Brothers
Fuel pipe	Old 20 Parts	Exhaust	Vintage Tractor Spares	Tires	Southern County Tractors

Family heirloom

Gary Connolly reports on a major Major restoration

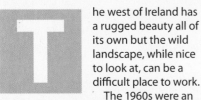

The west of Ireland has a rugged beauty all of its own but the wild landscape, while nice to look at, can be a difficult place to work.

The 1960s were an important decade in terms of infrastructure development in Ireland and there was a large electrification programme in particular. Many contractors worked for the local electrical supply company helping to roll out the power supply but the lines had to cross some difficult terrain and plant and equipment were tested to the limit.

Paddy Monaghan's father was one such contractor and, as a boy, Paddy remembers his father doing a lot of work all over Counties Galway and Mayo.

His father operated a bulldozer but purchased an industrial Fordson Major to work on some of the ancillary jobs such

as drilling holes for the telegraph poles.

The tractor had originally been operated by an English county council before being sold to Mr Monaghan by Henry Bower, of Somerset. Paddy still has the various letters sent to his father from the dealer detailing the shipping arrangements for it.

The tractor had originally been fitted with a snow plough but this was removed and replaced by a belt-driven welding set. The rear-mounted compressor was used to power the drill and other pneumatic equipment.

As time passed, there was less need for the Major in the civil engineering business and it was eventually parked up in the yard beside the dwelling house where it sat for many years, slowly deteriorating.

Paddy was keen to restore it and asked his father about it many times but it was always put on the longer finger. However, in 2006 permission was granted for Paddy to take

on the restoration and so a start was made.

The introduction of the "New Major" (officially designated the E1A Major) by Ford in 1951 was a milestone for the company. For the first time it was possible to purchase a Fordson tractor with a Ford diesel engine. The previous Major, the E27N, had been available with diesel power but only with a Perkins engine.

The project to develop a diesel engine for tractor power was initiated as far back as 1944 and, difficult as it might be to believe it today, there was considerable internal opposition within the company to the development of diesel power. Many at that time believed that petrol engines were the way forward.

New engine development was, and still is, a very expensive process but the engineers at Ford cleverly managed to minimise the cost by developing a suite of three engines - petrol, vaporising oil and diesel - which

The tractor was in a sorry state when Paddy convinced his father to let him restore it.

utilised the same core components.

Diesel had not been a popular choice for farmers up to the introduction of the Major, mainly due to the additional expense and a reputation for poor starting.

The new engine in the New Major was only marginally more expensive than the petrol or vaporising oil variants and proved to be easily started, rugged and extremely reliable. U

Production of the New Major continued until 1958 when the Power Major was introduced and total production exceeded 240,000, the vast majority of which were diesel models.

Paddy's industrial Major was one of a number of variants produced by Fordson during that era. As well as producing its own models, a large number of Major skid units were sold to companies such

as County and Roadless which in turn produced their own specialised tractors. Perhaps the most unique and memorable tractors based on the New Majors were the Doe Triple D machines, introduced in 1957, but that's another story.

Back to the restoration then. The tractor was by this stage in a very sorry state. Having limited mechanical experience, Paddy sought the advice of a friend who believed that, while it would take a lot of hard work, the tractor was still worth restoring.

Help was gathered and Paddy et al loaded up the tractor and took it to the shed where the "major" surgery could commence.

A friend did most of the mechanical restoration but many of the parts were beyond repair and Paddy ended up scouring the country and beyond for the missing pieces.

The more typical parts were sourced from local garages but Paddy resorted to the pages of T&M to find the more difficult pieces.

Dunlops from Ballymena and Richard Lewis in Wreham got a special mention from him. Richard, a Fordson specialist, was able to supply a bonnet and a fuel tank in good condition as well as a few other odds and ends.

Paddy's own background is not typical of many who restore tractors but his skill set has proved to be extremely useful. When the time came for him to leave school he decided against the plant work of his father and took a job in a furniture factory in Claremorris.

A similar job followed in another factory and, as his brothers left school, they joined the workforce in the factory also. When the

The rear pulley for driving the compressor replaced the normal pto shaft. The original compressor is still to be refitted but the unusual air storage tanks are a subject of interest and great debate whenever Paddy takes the tractor to a show.

The belt pulley was used by Paddy's father to drive a front-mounted welder.

factory closed it was a natural progression for the brothers to start their own business and they have now been in business for over 20 years, supplying bar furniture in Ireland and to the many Irish pubs which have proliferated all over the world.

For all of this time, among other roles, Paddy has been involved in spraying furniture and so he was well placed to complete the cosmetic aspect of the restoration.

When the mechanical work was completed the tractor and parts were sand-blasted and Paddy got down to the painting. The colour was mixed by a local supplier and based on the colour used by the English council for its livery.

Equipment from the factory was used to suspend the tractor above head height, a godsend as far as Paddy was concerned - "In 30 years of experience, it's the hardest thing I've ever sprayed. There were so many nooks and crannies."

It took a full day's work for him to apply the final top coat.

In real terms, the industrial version of the New Major was not a significant departure from the agricultural model. Paddy's tractor has an uprated rear axle and associated brakes and even those were available as an optional extra on the agricultural version.

The most obvious differences are a heavy front sub-assembly on to which a dozer blade or other front-mounted implement could be attached (since removed from Paddy's tractor) and the rear-mounted compressor with those unusual low slung air tanks.

The compressor has been removed from Paddy's tractor and is awaiting restoration but the tanks are an unmistakable feature of his tractor.

Paddy has been meticulous in recording the detail of the restoration and he kept all of the receipts associated with the work.

He was surprised at just how expensive the work was. "The paint alone cost over €400 while a new set of tyres set me back €930. Overall, the restoration cost €9,300 never mind the cost of my time."

Paddy has now had the tractor on display at a number of local rallies. Its next planned outing will be the local St Patrick's Day parade in March.

Now that the job has been virtually completed, what's next on the agenda?

Paddy laughed. "Now that my father has seen the tractor restored he wants me to do his old bulldozer but I think that's maybe a step too far!" ∎

NEW MAJOR SPECIFICATION

Cylinders	4
Bore x stroke	3.937in x 4.52in
Displacement	220cu in (3.6 litres)
Compression	16:1
Rated RPMs	1600
Horsepower	30hp @ drawbar (rated)
	34.2hp @ drawbar (max)
	35hp @ pto (rated)
Transmission	6 forward, 2 reverse
Options	Hydraulic linkage
	Two-speed pulley
	Rear pto shaft

NEBRASKA TEST 500

Test date	1953
Engine	Diesel
Belt	38.5hp (max)
Drawbar	34.2hp (max)

Nearside view of a nicely-preserved mid-Fifties tractor in original unrestored condition. This machine depicts the condition of tractors found in the 1970s. The air filter intake is under the bonnet and doesn't protrude through, giving clean lines!

A Major purchase

Andrew Hall profiles the Fordson Major Diesel for anyone considering a purchase here

rriving on the market in late 1951, the Fordson Major Diesel tractor (sometimes known as the New Major) was undoubtedly the most popular tractor introduction of the Fifties.

The seeds for the model were first sown with the introduction of the Fordson E27N, commonly known as the Fordson Major, in the spring of 1945 when demand for a tractor capable of pulling three furrows increased. E27N production ran from 1945 to early 1952 and overlapped the introduction of the E1A models.

Development of the E1A models was going on steadily whilst the E27N was in production and during this time the importance of diesel as the fuel for tractors became apparent because of its economy and ease of starting. Ford decided to develop a new engine range which could be built for petrol, TVO or diesel and would be suitable for both tractor and truck use.

It was the diesel version, known as the 4D, which became the power unit for the

Fordson Major Diesel, which eventually outsold the petrol and TVO variants. Other manufacturers developed their own diesel models and by the late 1950s the demand for petrol/TVO tractors had diminished.

This buyer's guide provides information and t ips for anyone considering purchasing a Fordson Major Diesel (E1ADDN) and overall the model's reliability, if serviced regularly, is extremely high which must have influenced the high sales throughout the production run from 1951 to 1958. Another positive point is the adaptability of the model, as there were many companies specialising in converting the models to undertake a plethora of tasks.

To clarify the designations the following table shows the models available.

Fordson Major	E1AD Petrol
Fordson Major	E1ADKN Kerosene (TVO)
Fordson Major	E1ADDN Diesel

ENGINE

The 4D engine fitted to the Major is a very robust and bulletproof unit, largely due to

the simplicity of the design. The engines are direct injection and, provided a good battery is fitted, will start readily in all weathers, even when worn excessively.

When inspecting an engine listen for any rumbling or knocking sounds from the bottom end, which may indicate excessively worn big end or main bearings. Fordson Major Diesel tractors have the luxury of an oil pressure gauge and the pressure on a good engine should be 30-40psi when cold. This may fall when hot but it is not significant. Many 4D engines have been known to run for many years with little or almost no oil pressure present before requiring a rebuild.

Withdraw the dip stick to inspect the colour of the oil. This should be black and not grey and sludgy as this may indicate a head gasket or cylinder liner problem. Early engines have only two bolts to secure the rocker cover and if the cover is slightly distorted leaks may occur down the engine, making things look worse than they really are. When the cover is fitted make sure it is in shape and use a new gasket! Engines used on later tractors (Mark 2 engine) have ▶

Offside view of the same machine. This tractor has the correct wheels fitted, unlike many. Note the 'big D' badge on the bonnet side and the belt pulley, which was a commonly-fitted accessory.

the securing screws around the edge of the cover and do not suffer in the same way.

Check the cooling system contents, which should have anti-freeze present, not only to prevent frost damage but also to avoid corrosion within the cooling jackets and cylinder liners of the engine. Engines merely drained of coolant as a protection from frost are vulnerable to corrosion of the cylinder liners which, in extreme cases, may 'pinhole' and allow water into the cylinders and cause the engine to hydraulic! This is where a piston cannot compress the water and prevents the turning of the engine. This is not the end of the road for these engines as the liners are of the 'wet' variety and are readily changeable.

Another point is the injection pump drive coupling, which consists of a fibre disc sandwiched between the drive flanges.

These tend to be noisy in operation and can break after many years service, but are readily available and easily replaced.

Although they are heavy to work on the 4D engines are easy to rebuild and do not present any specific challenges to anyone with a good knowledge of engines.

CLUTCH

Clutches on Diesel Majors are 11in diameter single plate dry or 13in if fitted with a heavy duty type. Provided the clutch is not abused and the free play is adjusted to manufacturer's settings many hours of service can be achieved before replacement.

Clutches on these tractors have weights to

This left-hand view of the engine shows the early wide fan belt. Later machines have a narrower belt. This is the regular position for the toolbox. The horizontal rod operates the radiator shutter, which was more important on the TVO version than the diesel.

Category two three-point linkage is fitted to this tractor, together with power take-off. These were optional extras at the time of manufacture, although many tractors were fitted with them, as the popularity of hydraulics and pto had risen by the mid-Fifties. This tractor has the early pan seat with the rubber cone for suspension.

Another left-hand shot of a different tractor. This has the later narrow fan belt and the air filter through the bonnet. This machine is also in good unrestored condition.

assist engagement when operating at high engine speeds and these must contribute to the long life! Only the last of the Diesel Majors, manufactured in 1957 prior to the Power Major in 1958, had the option of a dual clutch providing live drive to the pto and hydraulic pump: these have a clutch of 12in diameter and are limited in number.

GEARBOX AND REAR AXLE

The transmission of the Diesel Major was based on the earlier E27N design and has a constant mesh three-forward and onereverse gearbox with a two-speed high-low range box in front providing six forward and two reverse ratios. A belt pulley was available as an option and is on the righthand side of the transmission housing when fitted. Two speeds for this are available by selecting either high or low ratio on the range lever. If a pulley is fitted look for play in the bearings and failure of the oil seal, evident by the oil stain from the hub.

The gearbox is extremely robust and gives little trouble if lubricated properly. One feature of Diesel Majors, with the exception of the earliest built, is the parking brake which locks the transmission. The ▶

A view from the driver's seat of a working tractor showing the layout of the controls.

hand brake is mounted on the righthand side and, when applied, locks the transmission at the reverse gear idler.

This is a very efficient means of parking but care needs to be taken not to drive with the brake applied as this may cause the steel brake plates to seize and lock up permanently!

To undertake a repair on the brake requires the gearbox internals to be withdrawn through the clutch housing. Wear on the gear lever selector may be evident by sloppiness in the lever when engaged. The bronze selector pocket may be accessed and changed through the top of the transmission cover when the lever has been removed. The range lever needs to be tight on its splines. If not, it may slip and affect range changes and cause damage to the shaft.

Check the oil level within the gearbox at the filler cap near to the gear lever. Sometimes the oil seal between the gearbox and rear axle housing fails and the gearbox oil drains through to the rear transmission, raising the axle oil level, as the gearbox level is higher than the rear axle. This higher level often leaks out through the axle oils seals.

The rear axle is similar to the E27N and consists of a centrally-mounted differential driving bull pinion shafts. Spur reduction gears drive each half-shaft. Rear axles are fairly trouble-free. Look for failure of the previously mentioned oil seals on the outer ends of the axle. These require the top cover (hydraulic system) to be removed to access the inner ends of the axle shafts in order to access the oil seals

Instruments are housed in this control box which also contains the voltage regulator within. This remained unchanged until the arrival of the Power Major. The temperature gauge in non-original.

BRAKES

The braking system of the Diesel Major is a Girling drum system similar to the E27N, albeit on extensions of the bull pinion shafts to overcome oil seal problems encountered on the earlier model. The brakes are adequate for their purpose, provided they are adjusted properly and the operating cables lubricated and free. Grease nipples for the cables are accessed through the foot plates which may be packed with mud! Brake cables are often overlooked when servicing and may be seized through lack of use. New cables are available but are not cheap.

Access for engine maintenance is easy as is most of the fuel system, together with the battery, is on the right-hand side.

All Majors have provision for a belt pulley on the right-hand side of the clutch housing. When not fitted with a pulley a blanking plate is in place instead.

PTO AND HYDRAULICS

The power take-off is driven from the lower part of the gearbox and controlled by a lever mounted on the left-hand side of the gearbox casing. As most tractors have a single plate clutch there was no live drive available until the dual clutch models arrived. A speed of 540rpm is available at an engine speed of 1,200rpm which means that early models did not develop a high pto horsepower. An accessory, known as raised pto, could be added which lowered the ratio and provided 540rpm at 1,600 engine rpm, thus giving more power. Another bonus of the raised pto is that the shaft can be disconnected without disconnecting the drive to the hydraulic pump, which was always a shortcoming of the standard model. The term 'raised pto' refers to the fact that the shaft is mounted higher when the accessory is fitted. Tractors with this are worth seeking out! The hydraulic system consists of threepoint linkage with category two links but no draft control incorporated, as this was still covered by Ferguson patents at the time of introduction. Depth control for soil-engaging implements was mainly by means of depth wheels on the implements, but a pre-set linkage control could be fitted to restrict the lower limit of travel of the links. This fits to the right-hand link arm and can be adjusted by a hand wheel. As the linkage descends the adjustable link pushes the control lever into neutral and thus holds ▶

The correct rear wheels for all standard type Fordson Major Diesels have circular centres, rather than the scalloped centres of the Power Major.

Technical specification

Engine capacity 3,610 cc	
Horsepower 32.8 @ 1,400 RPM	
Fuel Diesel 15 gallons (68.25L)	
Engine Oil 12 Pints (6.816L)	
Cooling System 3 Gallons (13.64L)	
Gearbox 4.5 Gallons (20.43L)	
Rear Axle/	
Hydraulics 9 Gallons (40.91L)	
Weight (basic	
Tractor) 4,420lbs (2006Kgs)	
Length 130.5 inches (3.3m)	
Width 65 inches (1.605m)	
Height 63 inches (1.6m)	

Spares

The popularity of the Fordson Major Diesel means that spares availability is extremely good, with many spares still available from New Holland Dealers.

All plus VAT.
Other stockists include
Vapormatic (01392 684000)
for information of nationwide outlets.
Bepco (01299 252270)
for information of nationwide outlets.
Agriline: tel: 01527 579111
Dunlop Tractor Spares:
tel: 02825 652560
Southern Counties Tractor Spares
(01243 512109).

the implement at the desired depth. As with the raised pto, tractors with pre-set linkages control are worth having!

External hydraulic services are catered for by a single pipe which works in conjunction with the main control lever. An additional valve was an option which allowed independent operation of external services. Tractors with this feature have two levers side-by-side.

Overall, the system is reliable and has no specific weaknesses. Oil for the hydraulics is contained in the rear axle housing and amounts to approximately nine gallons (41 litres). If the oil is contaminated due to water emulsification it should be changed.

FRONT AXLE AND STEERING

The front axle is adjustable to provide varying track widths for specific jobs. Wear in the king pins and track rod pins may be evident on well-used tractors, particularly on tractors fitted with loaders. Look out for track arms welded to the kingpins where the splines have worn. The steering box is a robust recirculating ball design and longlasting; however. look for signs of oil leakage from the cross shaft on the left-hand side and also slackness. This can be adjusted by removal of shims. Collectively, wear can add up to steering wander and wheel wobble, but parts to repair this are available.

WHEELS AND TYRES

Standard wheels on the Diesel Major were 6.00-19 front cast centres and 11-36 pressed steel rears. Optional wheel sizes were 14-30 rear and 7.50-16 fronts, both pressed steel.

Many tractors today have the wrong wheel equipment fitted, particularly regarding the front cast wheels.

The correct centres for 1951 to 1958 are the four-hole centres with the dust ring incorporated around the hub, similar to late E27N machines. Many have ended up with three-hole centres, which should be fitted to the later Power and Super Major tractors.

Rear wheels should have circular dishes with no scallops. These did not arrive

until the Power/Super Major era. Cast centres are bulletproof and, provided the bearing is adjusted and lubricated correctly, are no problem. Rear wheels can suffer corrosion where in contact with manure, fertiliser etc. but rims are available as replacements if necessary.

TIN WORK

The new Fordson Major ranges were the first tractors produced by Ford in the UK with styled sheet metal. The styling is pleasing to the eye, particularly the early versions where the exhaust pipe was underslung and the air filter intake was under the bonnet.

Badging changed throughout production slightly. Early tractors have the name 'Fordson Major' on the bonnet sides with 'Diesel' on a separate badge below. From late 1954 the "big D" badge was used, until 1957 when Ford reverted to the 'Fordson Major' badge without the 'Diesel' below prior to the arrival of the Power Major.

Considering the earliest of these tractors is about 58 years of age there is bound to be some corrosion present unless one is lucky enough to obtain a tractor stored inside throughout its life. Weak spots are around the sides and top of the front cowl and the box sections and lower regions of the wings.

The spine of the bonnet is also vulnerable to corrosion. Replacement cowls are available in both steel and glass fibre together with bonnets and wings, but early tractors have different pattern wings which I am not sure are available yet.

Lighting was another regular feature of Diesel Majors. Early tractors had Butlers headlights and wing-mounted sidelights with one rear lamp centrally mounted on the rear axle. Later tractors had two rear lights on each wing.

PRICES

As with many other collectible tractors values have increased steadily in recent times. Rough tractors, including nonrunners, may be obtained from around £500, but expect to pay £1,000-plus for a running

machine requiring work. Tractors in top condition needing little or no work can be sought for £2,500 to £3,000. When viewing a tractor it is important to ensure it has its correct wheel equipment and is what is being advertised: if not this should be refl ected in the price.

CONCLUSION

The Fordson Major Diesel offers good value for money whether you need it for work or showing. The rugged design of the engine and transmission have proved to be a successful formula, demonstrated by many years of service! ■

Changing colour

Chris McCullough tracks down an MF man with a Fordson interest

When a devoted Massey Ferguson dairy farmer decided he wanted a Fordson Major in his collection all his friends and neighbours thought he was crazy.

Brian Hanna, from Ballymoney in County Antrim, runs an entirely red fleet on his farm and has quite an extensive range of classic and vintage Massey Fergusons in his tractor collection – including a nice original MF 65 which he has just added to it.

But his thoughts turned to owning a blue tractor and, in particular, a Fordson Major because he liked the look of them. Following a search lasting months Brian saw one advertised for sale in Kilkeel. It turned out to be a 1959 Fordson Power Major in traditional blue and orange colours, exactly what he was after, but needing a restoration.

"The tractor had obviously undergone a hard career and was most certainly in its working clothes," said Brian. "Although it was mechanically sound, the bodywork needed a lot of attention. Nevertheless, I liked the look

of it and bought it on the spot for £1,200."

Brian knew that both the front and rear rim centres were not original and that some of the dials were missing, but he knew he could have it restored back to original condition.

He said: "There were a few cosmetic issues with the Major but thankfully the engine and hydraulic system were fine. The rim centres on the rear were not the correct ones and the rims on the front should have been three-spoke versions."

Brian's friend and neighbour ▶

For a man with an addiction to the red and grey marque, Brian Hanna has done a good job of making sure that this Fordson Power Major lives on for many more years to come.

MRX 736

Brian was keen to get the details right – the effort has certainly paid off.

William Knox has tackled quite a few tractor restorations in his time. Although William usually spends most of his time hauling diggers around on his HGV, the current credit crunch has dictated a downturn in Northern Ireland's construction industry and this has had a knock-on effect on the need for haulage.

Never one to rest on his laurels William spends more time in the workshop now with quite a number of restoration projects going on at once.

He also has quite an extensive collection of tractors and plant machinery of his own so understood Brian's desire to restore the Fordson Major.

"Brian's only request to us was an order

to leave the tractor right," said William. "After removing all the tin work the tractor received a general mechanical overhaul. New bushings were fitted to the steering system to complete the functional side of the tractor. We decided to fit new mudguards and a new nose cone, too."

While the restoration was underway Brian was busy finding proper rims, which were fitted with new tyres to complete that part of the project. Luckily for Brian and William there is currently a plentiful supply of Major parts on the market so nothing was too hard to find.

After a complete spray job by William, including some extra attention to a 'stubborn' bonnet, which kept reacting to

paint, the tractor was almost complete. All it needed was Brian on the driver's seat.

William has a 1952 diesel Fordson Major of his own, which he restored, so completing Brian's Major was a comparatively easy task as he had some experience in the matter.

Brian's Major restoration took only one month to finish and the tractor has now joined his collection as only the second blue tractor in it – he also has a Ford 3610 but admits to having a grey wing Super Major on his most-wanted list.

The restoration cost a modest £1,200 to complete but the end result is both professional and breathtaking, leaving this traditionally 'red' man slipping into an emerging 'blue' man. ■

Brian (left) with friend and neighbour William Knox.

The amount of affection lavished on the tractor is obvious.

Romantic resto

Toby Ritchie explains why the family revived a Fordson Major

My brothers and I grew up on the family dairy/arable farm and, like most farmers' sons, we loved our tractors.

We used to get involved in everything we could but we all had a speciality. Paul, the eldest, didn't care much for the milking and was more interested in ploughing. Adam, the middle brother, spent most of his time sub-soiling and clambering up augers into some very questionable grain bins. I spent most of my time cultivating and looking after the calves.

Our machinery was mostly loyal to Ford. We had a 4000 (yard scraper), 5000, 6600 with Farmhand loader, 6600 dual power and a 6610.

In later years we bought a Massey 595 and then replaced that with our first 4WD, which was a 7610.

Our father and his parents had moved to the farm in the mid-sixties. It was larger than their previous farm so they invested in two Fordson Majors, one of which is the focus of this article.

She was used extensively on the farm as a main tractor and suffered a few battle scars - she had to be rewired due to her loom melting and the front cowl was bent from an incident with a hedge. There was also a rumour of our uncle driving her off the top of the silage clamp while rolling the grass.

Over the years she was demoted and ended up being a yard scraper until her clutch went and she was abandoned behind a building.

A local tractor enthusiast contacted my grandad in 1989 and expressed an interested in buying the Major for spares, but grandad said it wasn't for sale and that he had promised it to Paul.

Soon after his 13th birthday Paul decided to ask our dad to help him get the Major out of the bushes and running again so he could use it around the farm. Paul soon realised the tractor only had a few issues; the most serious job was evicting the mice that had moved into the cylinder head.

For the next ten years or so Paul used the Major whenever he did any work on the farm. It faultlessly performed many jobs, including ploughing, graining, carting and rolling.

In 1999 it was decided that the future of dairy farming was so unstable that it was not worth carrying on and the dairy herd was sold along with the majority of the machinery. Only the 7610, Major and Dexta were kept.

By this time Paul had left home and only returned to drive the Major occasionally.

It sat in one of the farm buildings gathering dust until last year when Paul announced he was getting married and the idea developed that it would be a great surprise if we secretly restored the Major.

The biggest problem was deciding when we could work on the tractor as Paul frequently visited the farm. Paul and Katie got married at the end of June, with their honeymoon immediately after the wedding. This gave us the opportunity to do the restoration without fear that Paul

The Major, on the Sunday, just after a tow start and prior to stripping down.

Some things took much longer than expected. When taking off the original link arms some of the pins were so worn they were difficult to remove. We ended up resorting to the brute force of a sledge hammer and blow lamp before they eventually gave in.

Paul had used many different tones of Ford blue over the years, so it was a novelty to see it in Fordson Empire Blue again.

would arrive at the farm unexpectedly.

The other problem was that Adam now lived in Aberdeen and would only be able to come down for a week to work on the Major, so to make more of a challenge for ourselves we aimed to do the restoration within the week following the wedding so that Adam could be fully involved and the Major completed in plenty of time for Paul's return.

The Sunday after the wedding we started at 6am and began by getting the Major's engine running for the first time in nearly a year. Then we spent the rest of the day stripping it down ready to be sand-blasted.

Some things took much longer than expected. When taking off the original link arms some of the pins were so worn they were difficult to remove. We ended up resorting to the brute force of a sledge hammer and blow lamp before they eventually gave in.

Once the tractor was completely stripped we hired a local tradesman to sand-blast the Major back to bare metal (Monday) and coated it in red oxide.

The next day I began repainting it in Fordson Empire blue. Paul had used many different tones of Ford blue over the years, so it was a novelty to see its original colour back.

We tried to retain as many original parts as possible, particularly the front cowl which required a lot of panel beating and welding to freshen up. However, we had prepared by going to the Old Sodbury sortout in anticipation of replacing some of the parts which we knew were beyond repair.

The Major also received numerous new parts including the wiring loom, front and rear lights, battery, seat, wings and footplates on the Wednesday.

Fitting new rubber was an expensive but necessary job, the old tyres were all mixed and perished. When the tyre

fitters arrived on the Thursday they showed a keen interest in the project but could not believe the time frame we were working to and how much progress had been made in just five days.

Adam spent a lot of time on the wiring, trying to get everything to work as it should. One problem occurred when it appeared that the generator and oil lights were working but we soon realised that at some point the generator wire had over-heated and fused to the oil pressure wire. The oil pressure switch was actually stuck and had not been working for a good number of years. Later, when we looked

at the photographs, we realised that by this stage in the restoration Adam had barely moved from this spot for three consecutive days, finishing on the Saturday.

By Sunday morning the whole restoration was complete and a couple of weeks later Paul and Katie returned from their honeymoon.

We surprised them with the restored Major and they immediately went for a drive around the fields, Paul grinning throughout.

The Major will now spend its time performing some light work and it may even venture to the odd ploughing match. ∎

Six days later the Major had been completed and looked resplendent.

It's new and blue

Peter Squires reports on the latest creation from Nottinghamshire's John Hayward!

John Hayward likes to take something different to Southwell ploughing match each year. In 2007 it was a Fordson Triple-Power and in 2008 it was the Martrac – the Major Articulated Tractor.

The design came from a Matbro Mastiff after his friend Rhodes Waterhouse challenged him to "build one of those."

John said: "I looked at what I thought the Mastiff lacked and how progress could have improved it.

"It was built by a company that built forklifts, not tractors, it had no pto shaft and although it had a six-cylinder engine, it lacked a heavy-duty linkage.

"The operator's position was high but narrow - one slip and you were on the ground – and I preferred the longer wheelbase of the Triple-Doe (120 inches between axle centres) to the Mastiff."

John drew up his spec. Engine, Ford 508E six-cylinder with a Holset turbo and oil cooler; gearbox, Fordson Major (standard); transmission, two Fordson Super Major transmission units back-to-back to give optional 4WD; gears, 12 forward, three reverse using two separate Hi-Low shifts; power steering, articulated via two rams (one either side); Live-Drive.

A Casappa twin-compartment gear-driven pump is fitted to the front of the tractor and, working off the crankshaft pulley, it delivers 2,500psi for the hydraulic lifts; the pump's second compartment delivers less pressure for the two steering rams.

From the diagram you can see the drive is taken straight out of the gearbox. The pto drive is from the Major's pto transfer unit in the gearbox. Drive is then taken down vertically via a duplex chain in a transfer box that John made.

The bottom sprocket then takes the drive horizontally through the front transmission unit (this unit being reversed), passing to the rear transmission unit (facing forward) via a universal-jointed propshaft. The drive then passes through

the rear unit to the pto output shaft.

The centre of the Martrac is articulated, both halves being held together by two pins incorporated into the framework. The universal-jointed propshafts (one for the pto, one for the transmission drive) take the drives over the articulated section.

Two centrally-positioned hydraulic rams steer the machine via power steering.

Drive to the axles is taken directly from the gearbox through a shaft passing directly under the driver's seat over the front transmission unit to a second transfer box. Drive is then taken vertically downwards through helical gears in the transfer box, being then directed horizontally both fore and aft into the two transmission housings.

John has fitted an Airshift compressed air system to engage/disengage the 4WD.

In two-wheel drive the Martrac runs on the rear axle but operating a small lever beside the driver operates a drive dog which engages the lower helical gear in the second transfer box and the forward transmission is brought into operation. Flick

At Southwell Show on 27th September, Thomas Waterhouse puts the Martrac through its paces at the Southwell ploughing match.

Above: Impressive from any angle!

Left: The uni-jointed sliding propshafts for both the final drive and pto shafts bridge the articulated section.

Below right: The heart of the Martrac is its Ford 508E six-cylinder engine.

Key made a stainless steel exhaust and Thomas Waterhouse fabricated side covers to give the Martrac a stylish line.

The Martrac has four single spool valves and one double.

When it came to the test run John was a little nervous because nothing like this machine had been tried before.

A five-furrow Ransomes plough was coupled up and Thomas Waterhouse eased the machine into the field. After a few runs up and down the field, the verdict was delivered. Perfect!

The Martrac was pressure washed and the spray-gun filled with paint.

At Southwell the machine again proved perfect, hauling its five-furrow plough the full distance of the field throughout the day before a good crowd of curious onlookers.

Smoke from the Ford engine was almost invisible, the turbo singing yet hardly working the engine in the damp but hard ground.

I asked Thomas what it was like to drive and operate.

He said: "In two-wheel drive it struggles, but it slips into 4WD easily and every single horsepower is on the floor. It's easy to drive and control and does what it is supposed to."

John Hayward was very pleased with his Martrac's performance, probably feeling he had corrected what he wanted to of the Matbro Mastiff design.

So will there be something else new for the next Southwell match? ∎

A Danfoss switch is connected to operate the compressor and regulates the pressure in the receiver tank.

A radiator fan surround had to be made to clear the 18-inch diameter fan blade.

The throttle lever to the Simms pump is vertical, not in the usual Super Major position beside the steering column.

A heavy-duty rear linkage was fabricated for the Martrac. The diff-lock is hydraulically operated.

The front unit's disc brakes are worked hydraulically by a master cylinder, with a separate master cylinder to the rear unit's brakes, which are standard Super Major disc brakes.

Steel plate (20mm thick) was plasma-cut for the top and bottom of the Martrac's framework, 12mm for the sideframes and the front.

To cap the hybrid machine off, Nick

the switch back and 4WD is disengaged.

A second lever works the 2:1 ratio. This halves the road speed via the transfer drive box and effectively gives the machine another six forward and two reverse speeds, the standard Hi-Lo lever working as normal.

The Airshift operates from a small 12-volt compressor, which is fitted just inside the frames of the front section and works off the tractor battery. The pump is designed to run at 150psi but John has lowered it to 100psi.

An air receiver tank is fitted behind the driver's seat with an air pressure valve and spare instant connector (just in case anyone needs a tyre inflated)!

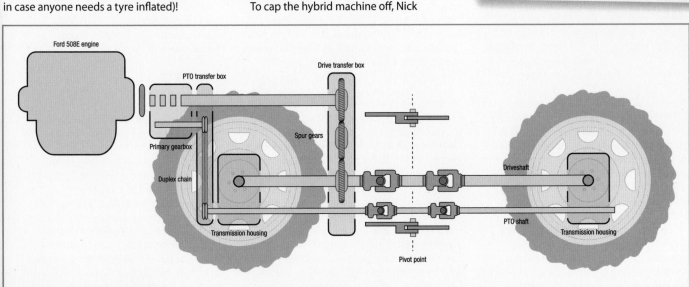

A diagramtic section of the Martrac and its major components.

The Kiwi Crane seen prior to Malcolm Beaton's autumn sale.

(l-r) Gary Barnard and Bernard Saunders with the 1964 Kiwi.

Hudson 'Kiwi'

Apart from pulling power and working the land, Fordson Major tractors were often used as the motive power behind various conversions including the rare Hudson 'Kiwi' Crane. Peter Squires spends a day with a recent owner.

The Hudson 'Kiwi' was designed as a simple yard crane which utilised the reliable power of the Fordson Major tractor for its operation. Not a great deal of information is available on the Kiwi, however, there is a basic knowledge available of its designer Robert Hudson.

Robert gained much of his engineering skill from his family who were the owners of the local Victoria Colliery in Bruntcliffe, Morley, and he designed machines to make the miner's life more bearable.

Robert founded his company, Robert Hudson Ltd, in 1865. It was based in Gildersome, near Leeds and grew to become a major international supplier of light railway materials, equipment and construction machinery required to develop Britain's growing railway network. The company name was later changed to Robert Hudson (Raletrux) Ltd.

GREAT NORTHERN

To improve access to the Hudson works a new rail connection with the Great Northern Railway main line from Wakefield to Bradford was established in 1890 to allow delivery of raw materials and finished goods to be transported by rail to the growing industrial areas. A head office, which was the main sales and design centre, was later established in Meadow Lane, Leeds; which was ideal for customers arriving by rail.

During the 1950s Hudsons recognised the threat to its business in the construction machinery industry from more modern rubber-tyred roadtype vehicles. To meet this challenge the company introduced its own range of road vehicles starting in 1960 with the Leedsall dumper truck. This was followed by the Kiwi crane and the Timiser low loading trailer. Initially, these developments provided replacement work for the declining orders for railway equipment. To consolidate this, a Contractor's Equipment division was formed in 1964. The declining

railway business finally took its toll in 1984 when the company was liquidated.

Several Kiwi Cranes were constructed around the Ford 5000, but this is the first Fordson Major-based example I have heard of.

THE BASICS

The tractor used in this particular Kiwi conversion is a 1964 Super Major (08D 970746) purchased by Bernard Saunders of Farnsfield from the Malcolm Beaton auction in November 2007. Bernard gave me an exclusive insight as to how the machine worked and to what he thought of its operation.

He went on to explain: "The tractor is fitted with a down-swept exhaust while the hydraulic steering rams and crane jib are operated from an oil pump and hydraulic oil reservoir both fitted to the front weight block of the tractor. The basic cab design even has the luxury of a heater fan, worked off the water hoses."

The steering control operating lever is on the right of the cab (black knob) the jib raise lower (red knob).

Turning right, the left-hand ram extended forcing the rear-half to the left. Note the oil reservoir for the rams in front of the nose cone.

The turning circle of the crane is governed by two hydraulic rams fixed to a frame and pivoted from underneath the tractor gearbox. The Kiwi is steered by a lever which turns the front axle to either the left or right via the two rams. The lever, which replaced the Major's steering wheel, is situated in the cab on the right-hand side along with the crane jib lever, which controls up and down movement.

"To turn the crane to the left, the operator pushes the control handle forward. This movement extends the right-hand (off-side) ram, forcing the rear half of the Kiwi to the right," Bernard explained. "To turn right, the control handle is pulled backwards, extending the left-hand ram, forcing the rear-half to turn left. A similar principle to a Triple Doe."

HEAVY-DUTY CRADLE

The front axle is fitted on an 'A' frame, pivoted under the tractor gearbox. This axle with the 'A' frame is rigid whilst the engine, gearbox and rear wheels are forced by the steering rams into a turning circle which is approximately 12 feet in radius. A heavy-duty cradle is fitted around the engine. This has two pivots in one vertical centre-line, the top pivot pin is for the boom and the bottom for the ram pivot, making the boom turn with the tractor.

The jib of the crane is of fixed length (non-extending) and is fitted with two hooks, one of which is heavy-duty, capable of lifting 8500lb, while the other is light for more general yard and unloading duties. Bernard observes: "the Kiwi is capable of lifting a Fordson Major engine with ease and can transport it around the yard. I feel, due to the construction of the Kiwi, that it could have probably lifted the whole tractor too." ∎

Lots of weight at the back!

Bernard uses the 'lightweight' hook to lift a Major front axle.

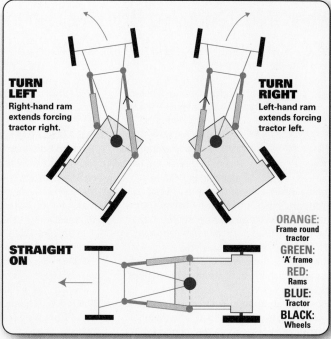

TURN LEFT
Right-hand ram extends forcing tractor right.

TURN RIGHT
Left-hand ram extends forcing tractor left.

STRAIGHT ON

ORANGE: Frame round tractor
GREEN: 'A' frame
RED: Rams
BLUE: Tractor
BLACK: Wheels

A Major vinyard where vintage is best

The old dependable Fordson Majors just seem to keep on working effortlessly and relentlessly in our forests, woods and woodyards. The first light-blue Fordson Majors were introduced to Britain during 1951, and what a testimony to British engineering and design that so many Majors are still hard at work more than 50 years on.

Woodyard owner Richard Wilks says that he is a true believer in the light-blue Majors for several reasons. He can clearly remember his grandfather and father working with Majors on the mixed dairy arable farm at Bewdley, Worcestershire, and secondly, he still uses two Majors in his business, and one of them has been in the family for a half-century.

Today Richard runs a landscape material supplies business offering anything from soil to various types of stone, to woodchips as well as hardwood firewood supplies. His main aids are two Fordson Majors – one, a 1953 Diesel Major which the family purchased in 1958, while the other is a 1964

New Performance Super Major acquired by Richard around ten years ago.

THE FAMILY FARMYARD
The yard from which Richard operates today was the family farmyard and buildings where he grew up. As with many small farms, the families had to look for alternative, often essential, second incomes to subsidise the farm.

In the mid-1980s Richard and his family wound down the farming operation and established a new business utilising the well-equipped yard and buildings.

Richard's grandfather, Thomas Nellis Wilks, purchased his first Fordson Major from the South Shropshire Fordson dealer, Leslie P. Morris, in

Richard Wilks.

The New Performance Super Major works to earn its keep.

The Super Major is key to the wood-cutting business.

1958. At the same time he was offered and purchased a Fordson Major on County half-tracks, which replaced an ageing Marshall crawler when more power was required on the farm.

The half-track was an exceptional tractor and allowed the Wilks family to keep working when all those around them had to stop. The land around Bewdley is fine in summer, but once winter arrives the land becomes waterlogged; the ground just becomes so heavy. The crawler could travel on the fields without sinking or doing damage, and the farm workers could harvest manglewurzels and other fodder root crops in all weathers. The crawler was also used for towing the other tractors out of the fields.

TRACKS SOLD FOR SCRAP
Retired around 20 years ago the halftrack was parked up in a shed and sadly, the tracks were sold for scrap. The tractor still has the original engine and it is Richard's aim to restore the tractor fully as soon as he can find another set of tracks, so if anyone knows of a set for sale, call Richard on 07813 093803.

The red wheel Major that is still used in the business was fitted with a new

half-engine in 1964, which increased the tractor's power to that of the Power Major. The Major ran troublefree for a further 30 years before the liner seals went and the engine underwent an overhaul.

Today the Major, registration JNT 821 is still going strong and is used mainly with a transport box mounted on the rear for moving logs, stone, sand and other bulky material around the yard. Richard says: "This Major may be a workhorse, but I do enjoy taking it on road runs and going to local shows and working days. The Fordson Majors are great tractors which have a great deal of appeal for numerous people. Quite often my customers find it hard to believe that I am still using tractors that have worked and been operated by three generations of one family over a 50-year period."

For the logging side of the business the New Performance Super Major is called into regular use, fitted with a Japa firewood processor. Richard says that a 30hp machine could easily operate the Japa, the main problem is weight distribution: "The Japa

is quite a heavy machine when lifted on the rear link arms. The Major is heavy at the front end and is ideally matched to this machine, whereas a smaller tractor would need plenty of front end weight added."

He continued: "The firewood side of the business does keep me very busy. We have corded hardwood timber delivered, mainly ash, oak and sycamore. I then saw the timber into logs and with the splitter, on a good day I can process around three quarters of a tonne of timber an hour."

'WE ARE A TEAM'
The Fordson Majors are invaluable to Richard: "These tractors are reliable and always start first time. They are very cheap to run and above all, are easy to service and maintain. The only drawback is if it is wet and windy you are exposed to all the elements. But why should I change to more modern tractors that cost more to run and are not as easy to service and repair as the older tractors. When I have finished work I can simply unhitch the various pieces of kit behind them and enjoy joining my friends on road runs and the like."

"I know there is a lot of talk at the moment of a 1961 Fordson Super Major fetching big money, I heard of one recently going for £12,650; but if I sold mine I would have to spend all that on a new machine which may not be as reliable. I know the history of my machines, they work well for me, and we are a team," affirmed Richard. ∎

The Fordson Major is mainly used with a transport box.

Never say no

Arthur Bliss writes about the tractor no-one wanted

Darren Harper works for Mereworth Estates in Kent as a game keeper and has been a 'blue' tractor fan since he was a small boy.

He spotted a Fordson Power Major in Freddie Smith's scrapyard at Mereworth, which he was keen on, but many people had looked at the tractor and they all said no: it was missing many parts, including the bonnet, had the wrong wheels fitted and looked a total wreck.

However, he bought it for £600 and when he started it with a new battery it ran very well. In fact, the engine number dates from 1960 so there is a strong possibility it had been changed.

All the filters and oils were changed and, despite the vehicle having looked a mess, the mechanical side was in excellent condition and the engine didn't need any work.

The same applied to the steering; the correct period cast spoke wheels were found and David Chamberlain, a Roadless County Major owner who knows his Fords through and through, came up with the correct bonnet.

New tyres and tubes were applied front and rear besides new wings, a new nose cone and a steering wheel, which came from Southern Counties Spares, and a new wiring loom.

Last August the paintwork was all sanded down because Darren does not believe in sand-blasting; he says the damage it does is not worth all the hassle in the long term.

On went various coats of quick-drying primers, followed by three coats of Empire Blue - and the finish is excellent for a first effort. Even the exhaust is correctly painted blue (but the grille sieves are painted red when they should really be silver).

The hydraulics work well, bits are being added all the time and this example doesn't carry a lighting kit, but in time that is to be added, I am sure. ■

Tom's trio of Fordsons, all of which were manufactured between 1960 and 1964.

Wood working fordsons

Out go the pigs; in come the tractors. Alan Turner reports

Southmead is the place Tom Broad has called home for the last 31 years - as do some members of his family, assorted livestock and three Fordson tractors.

The smallholding is at the foot of Ditchling Beacon, one of the highest points on the South Downs just north of Brighton, but the arrangement of neat gardens and homely bungalows is a far cry from the basic accommodation with which he started and a testament to the impressive energy of the recently-retired Sussex man.

Tom's main source of income was working for South East Water's various sub-contractors, including Pipeway, with whom he stayed for 12 years.

However, his plans to develop Southmead required additional cash, a potential source of which was the logging trade.

Tom's father had a logging business in nearby Burgess Hill and two acres of woodland at the Sussex village of Wivelsfield where a Fordson Power Major and a saw bench were the basic tools of a successful business.

Tom started his own logging business and combined it with an interest in older vehicles. As well as continuing the family

faith in Fordson tractors, a mainstay of the logging business was a 1939 AEC Matador.

Once a heavy recovery vehicle, its rugged construction made it ideal for crossing cleared forest land to retrieve timber. It arrived in a dilapidated state but was virtually complete and help with the restoration came from one of the local showmen, who had retained a supply of Matador spares.

Tom's logging business became a useful source of funds for his ambitions but its season only runs from September to around January so he supplemented his income with pig farming for a while.

His lorry was frequently seen humming along the A27 with loads of surplus loaves, skimmed milk, McCain oven chips and even Mars bars to feed them.

The Fordsons came into their own here. As well as doing the basic unloading and moving of foodstuffs, a special attachment, designed and made by Tom, provided the means to stir up some of the ingredients into pig food.

But late one night, while he was still attending to the pigs and with the prospect of having to rise for work in too few hours, Tom decided the pigs had become too much of a liability. They went and the building now houses his tractor collection.

Tom remains faithful to his Fordsons and his collection comprises three examples, all manufactured between 1960 and 1964. Registration number 349 OBP (08D 956058650) was bought from Bill Kerr, an agricultural contractor who was based outside Gatwick. The tractor was in fairly good order. u

The Fordson Super Major, 73 LOR (08C 949735) has become a rolling

Tom Broad.

restoration. It was offered for sale in the local free ads paper and swift action secured it at a good price.

Recently, the tractor has been driving the saw bench as Tom and the family have prepared another small mountain of logs for the winter season.

For a while, it was laid up as restoration work was curtailed and wagtails took advantage of the hiatus to build a nest - and so work was further postponed until the fledglings were gone. Tom observes, with a wry smile, that they seem to have taken half the tractor's wiring with them. Electrics were the source of a number of minor problems as they re-commissioned the tractor.

The third example is 08D 266151. This was bought from a timber merchant in Wivelsfield, who also favoured Majors for his forestry work. He had a reputation for working his tractors to death in the woods but Tom managed to save this one and it appears to have had the clutch replaced fairly recently.

Above: The mainstay of Tom Broad's business is the long-serving 1939 AEC Matador. It was once a heavy recovery vehicle making it ideal for crossing cleared forest land to retrieve timber.

Left: The Matador has received a few cosmetic changes. The locally made front bars are ideal for forestry work and the flashing beacon is useful to make other road users aware of the vehicle. The lorry has also been adorned with Fordson blue - adding a touch of uniformity to Tom's fleet.

Tom and his co-restorer, son-in-law Jason 'Taff' Mathias, explained the routine for cosmetic maintenance as working tractors soon look a little tired.

In summer time, well away from the logging season, a coat of the familiar Fordson blue is applied. The tractor is jacked up, placed on axle stands and the wheels are removed for painting separately. Everything is left in the sun to warm and Taff reckons the paint will cure sufficiently for handling within four hours.

The front cowling always seems to suffer badly on the Fordsons and so this is replaced along with the grilles, which also tend to expire. The bonnets have a hard life, but have been saved with just a bit of attention to the hinges. The mudguards may also require replacement.

Tom says that keeping the tractors purely as a hobby is an expensive prospect, but by using them to support the business, expenses can be offset and the cost justified.

He surveys the building that houses the current collection and muses on where he could find space for more tractors. His next project will be a Major, of course, but it could well be more ambitious as he relishes a further challenge.

He already has a spare engine and this may well be stripped and overhauled purely for the challenge. ∎

Darrell and son Francis with the resplendent 1964 Super Major.

It's for my dad

You never forget the first one, as Darrell Williams proves

In 1964 a Fordson New Performance Super Major was bought new from George Oakley's, of Market Drayton, and delivered to Mr HB Brown's Newtown Farm, Audlem, near Nantwich, Cheshire.

It was put straight to work spreading muck, ploughing, baling, sowing, hedge cutting and spraying.

My late father Bernard Williams was the head tractor driver at Newtown Farm at the time and, as a child, I watched him doing many tasks on the Major - in particular I remember going to see him plough a field one very cold winter's morning in the early '70s.

He had a big army coat on, two pairs of gloves, a bobble hat and Hessian bags on his legs to keep warm. We took him a warm drink and he got off the tractor

and undid one side of the bonnet and got under it as best he could to get a little warm. I thought at the time that I'd drive that tractor one day but it would have to be when the weather was warmer!

After 24 years of being the main tractor, the Major was put on lighter duties as my father took delivery of a new International Harvester with a cab.

That meant I got my first go on the Major. I backed up to the roller with help from my Uncle Frank and set off rolling and chain harrowing field after field. I drove her most days from then on, mostly scraping the yard. It was a struggle to reach the pedals in the early days but I managed and it got easier as I grew older.

Then in 1982 I left school and didn't see the old girl until January 2007 when I got a call from Newtown Farm asking if I knew anyone who would be interested in buying her.

I thought my birthdays had all come

at once! I had a six-cylinder 1963 Super Major at the time but thought of all the memories of my father and myself driving that old Major so I said "yes."

I struck a deal and brought her home. I thought that any minute I would wake up to find it had all been a dream. But it was not.

My task was to bring her back to her former glory but I had my work cut out because there was very little tin work that was any good, there was oil leaking out of every seal and there was about 44 years of muck and grime to shift.

The first job was to steam-clean the tractor all over then I stripped it down to nothing. I fitted new oil seals all round but when it came to fitting the rear hub seals the bearing just fell to pieces when I drew the shafts out so new bearings were fitted.

The engine and back end were fine - no knocks or bangs, they all worked great so I just dropped the oils, fitted new

After steam-cleaning, the Fordson begins to show some of its original blue colour.

filters and put new oils in. A new pair of king pins and bushes was also fitted.

Then it was time to tackle the 44-year-old tin work. This is where my mate Alan came in and I bet at the time he wished he hadn't offered to do it: the tin work was bad.

But he got stuck in like a good 'un and took it back to bare metal. It was given three coats of primer and three top coats of New Performance blue then the wings, wheels and the nose cone grilles were painted in Fordson grey.

What a transformation! It looked great, so it was time to put her back together and on February 8, 2008, my wife put the nose cone emblem on that she had just painted and it was finished.

All that was left was to fill the fuel tank, bleed the pump, turn the key and up she fired - born again! Then I put the road tax on and off I set on my test run.

One of the first journeys I made was to the place where the Major started its working life at Newtown Farm, where Mr Brown was shocked to see the old Super Major back to her former glory. He said it looked just like it did when he bought it in 1964.

After a long chat and a cup of tea it was time to set off back home. It was a weird feeling - it was the first time I had driven this tractor properly for 36 years and it took me back to my childhood.

I wondered what my father must have felt like driving it back in 1964, knowing

that it arrived new of April 13, 1964, which was his birthday. He would have been 24 and what a great birthday present - to be at work and take possession of this fine tractor must have been the best present ever.

The test run was a success so now my wife Rebecca, son Francis and I can get ready for shows and many road runs. This tractor is my pride and joy.

I would like to thank Mr Brown for selling her to me and Alan Unsworth, who had his work cut out with all the rubbing-down, sand-blasting, knocking-out 44 years of dents and hours of painting. Most of all I thank my wife and son for putting up with not seeing me for 12 months while I was in the garage working on the tractor.

Restored in memory of the late Bernard Henry Williams – my dad! ∎

It's amazing how a coat of primer can instantly transform a tractor isn't it?

The operator's platform looks as inviting as it would have done to Bernard in 1964.

All about Eve!

A rare site indeed, four 1964 Super Major FMF8 tractors.

Peter Squires recently came across a line-up of strange-looking green Fordson Major conversions, which had been adapted for a specific job undertaken by Eve Construction. Intrigued by what he saw, further investigations were necessary.

Founded in 1930 as JL Eve Construction, the Eve Group has evolved from its humble beginnings as a traditional rigging contractor to become a specialist provider of turnkey network infrastructure services, an undisputed leader in its field. Next time you see electric wires and pylons running across the countryside, just spare a little thought for the men who erect the wires which instantly supply electricity to your homes at the flick of a switch.

One vehicle used for this work from the 1950s onwards was the Auto-Mower 'FMF8' winch tractor. FMF stood for Fordson Major Front-mounted winch, and '8' referred to the gears of the winch – eight forward, two reverse – giving rope speeds of from two foot per minute to 160 ft per minute.

AUTO-MOWER
The history of the FMF8 goes back to Auto-Mower of Bath, who in 1956 were asked to design a winch tractor for Balfour Beatty, for the use of laying and connecting power

Rob Sonnex, Mechanical Plant Manager at Balfour Beatty, Raynesway.

lines to the Shetland Isles, which until then had a very limited electricity supply to remote areas. The popular, powerful and reliable Fordson Major was used as the starting point, which was greatly modified by Auto-Mower. The front axle was removed and an extended chassis fitted. A fabricated heavy-duty front axle was constructed to take a pair of 12.4 x 36" rear wheels and tyres; the Major's own rear tyres were substituted for industrial 16.9 x 14-30 tyres! This gave the tractor improved steering and grip and traction – vital given the harshness and rigours of the Shetlands landscape, which it managed well.

Robbie Howieson, Foreman Fitter at Eve, Notts.

BACK TO BEATTY!
I visited Balfour Beatty who still has a range of Ford 7810 tractors adapted for "sagging" and positioning the huge hydraulic capstan winches on electric pylon work. I spoke to Rob Sonnex, Mechanical Plant Manager for Balfour Beatty in Raynesway, Derby

He explained the basic principles of how power cables are hung between the massive pylons and the tractor's involvement: "Basically the new cable is attached to the old cable (still on the pylon).

The pulling winch hauls the old cable along the pylons via pulleys and off onto a drum. The new cable is pulled

Note the engineer in the basket working on the pylon arm in conjunction with the County on the ground.

Sadly due to H&SE legislation, many of these amazing workhorses have only just been laid up.

along the pylons until it reaches the drum, where it is then disconnected and connected up to the main power line. The tractors would be used for lifting and lowering the man working platform and cable pulleys onto the pylon arms. The strange 'A' frame over the tractor was used in conjunction with a mast for lifting cable drums full of electric cable, or lifting the conductor boxes up to the pylons."

Rob continued: "The front-mounted drum could be used to pull three different ways. A straight pull from the front of the tractor, the cable routed underneath the tractor to be pulled out from the rear, cable pulled in towards the rear of the tractor (idler rollers were positioned inside the extended side frames to prevent rope 'slap' on the tractor's underbelly). Or the winch rope could be slung over the 'A' frame rollers above the tractor enabling a straight vertical lift. Auto-Mower fitted an anchor to the tractors rear when a 'rear pull' was being carried out."

AT EVE!

Eve are still heavily involved with power transmissions and I visited Robbie Howieson at the Newton, Notts base, where several Fordson Majors, Ford 5000s and even a 6610 model were in the yard.

Robbie has been with the company since 1973 as a foreman plant fitter. "The older Majors have either Ford or BMC gearboxes fitted to the winch for controlling the winch speed, although the BMC box is better as the Ford boxes are older and worn. The BMC gearboxes are around a good ten years younger. The winch gears are selected with a large crude control rod resting on the 'A' frame near the operator, but with the 5000 models the winch is fully-controlled by hydraulics," Robbie told me.

"The only problem encountered on the older Majors is the steering box. This is still the same as fitted to the standard Major, although there is a lot more stress on the steering box having the longer heavy-duty steering rods and equal-size front wheels giving a larger turning circle. I've worked on several Majors with remote ▶

A pre-force Ford 5000 now retired from its duties.

This shot was taken in Argentina and shows and FMF8 lifting a cable drum.

steering boxes fitted to the chassis. What they are off I've no idea but perhaps this was an Auto-Mower solution to the wear problem."

The winch drum controls were perhaps a bit archaic and crude, but they worked. A gear wheel was fitted where the normal belt pulley roller would be fitted on the side of the tractor, driving a heavy-duty chain to the winch gearbox, which was situated above the actual winch drum. This had a short gear lever protruding, controlled by a large length of steel bar (about ten feet) with notches. This was pulled and pushed until the gear speed for the winch drum was obtained! A second steel lever resembling a very large handbrake lever on the tractors nearside controlled the drive-dog to put the winch gearbox either in or out. No messing about, you were either in or out of gear, drum either rotating or not.

The tractor clutch pedal was used in conjunction with the gear-change lever and drive dog lever. There were no 'posh' hydraulics to ease gently in or out, perhaps this was the eventual reason for the tractors being failed by the Health & Safety boys, together with the large chain and gear- drive system!

Archaic or not, the Auto-Mower system worked perfectly well (coupled with the operator's skill). Transmission companies, firms such as Balfour Beatty, AMEC and Eve Construction used the Fordson Major 'FMF8' tractors with great success for many years.

COUNTY POWER FORAMEC!
Around June 2006 AMEC have been contracted to work on a National Grid

Mick Jones on AMECs 1174 County manoeuvring cable pulleys up onto the pylon arms.

contract, replacing the 4ZV route of 275Kv cabling from High Marnham power station in Nottinghamshire as far as Chesterfield in Derbyshire. AMEC have several high-powered tractors available for winching, but the pylon I visited had the perfect machine – a 1978 County 1174 fitted with hydraulic T.H. Whites (Auto-Mower) winches. The tractors are used for positioning the huge "cable pullers" in the field, for raising or lowering the pulleys, insulators and working platform during installation work and for generally moving equipment around the field.

Each pylon arm had four cables connected to it via the conductors. Two cables with new insulators were replacing the existing four cables.

Once the pulleys were raised to the pylon arms by tractor winch the new cables were attached to the old. The old cables were attached to the "puller" capstan winch-drums and hauled in.

The new cables were drawn over the pylon pulleys until all the new cable was drawn along the pylons, the old cable being wound off onto cable reels. Mick Jones was operating the County 1174 as the AMEC gang reached Palterton in Derbyshire: "We prefer this tractor to the newer models. It's got plenty of power for what we need and is reliable! The old Majors were known as 'queer yokes' because they looked strange and were yoke (anchor) tractors!"

In Ollerton Nottinghamshire, 20 miles from the Palterton gang, a 2006 New Holland TS100A used a pair of Ulrich winches to lower and raise the pulleys and insulators, showing that from the first choice of Fordson over 60 years ago, Ford, County and New Holland are still a preferred power source for this type of work! ∎

Modern power, a 2006 New Holland TS 100A fitted with Ulrich winches front and rear working at Ollerton, Nottinghamshire.

The Ford 7810 became a very popular tractor for cable work and are still regularly called on.

The F.M.F.8 Auto Winch

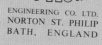

An Indispensable Tool for

CONSTRUCTIONAL ENGINEERS

TIMBER MERCHANTS

CONTRACTORS

A uto-Mower's history dates back many years to 1922, a time when the fledgling company was adding petrol engines to mechanical push lawn mowers. This was quickly followed by adapting wind turbines used for pumping water to be driven by small petrol-driven engines and orders flooded in.

With the introduction of the Fordson Standard N and the onset of the Second World War, Auto-Mower from Norton St. Philip in Somerset developed various winches and timber lorries built around the 'N' to assist with the war effort by speeding up the timber harvest of the UK's forests and for the Fleet Air Arm and the Air Ministry for towing aircraft.

Auto-Mower was employing over 200 staff at that time with many private industries after the War placing orders for tractors fitted with winches for all types of operations from constructional engineers to contractors. In 1956 Auto-Mower was commissioned to design a winch tractor for Balfour Beatty, for the use of laying and connecting power lines to the Shetland Isles, which until then had a very limited electricity supply to remote areas. Auto-Mower and Balfour Beatty combined forces to develop the highly-successful '8-speed, Heavy Duty Auto-Winch' with the Fordson Major being the starting point.

NEW IN ITS FIELD

The new machine was named the 'F.M.F.8' Auto Winch, which represented something entirely new in its field and was found to be invaluable in constructional engineering and other industries where a need existed for a highlymobile, heavy-duty winch, with a wide range of rope speeds. One example was that of tensioning overhead hightension cables, in this task it proved greatly successful in both its quality of work and considerable cost savings over previous methods.

The winch gave a 10-ton pull direct off the drum and its eight forward and two reverse gears provided rope speeds of 160 ft per min to 2ft per min. An internal expanding drum brake of the latest design was located on the pinion shaft, which was extremely powerful in operation and readily operated by hand from the driver's seat.

The mobility of the F.M.F.8 was quite remarkable, its 11.00 x 36 front tyres enabled it to be driven over ground which in the past would have been considered only possible by a tracked vehicle, nor was this obtained at the expense of its steering qualities, in fact it was claimed it steered as well as many cars of the day and with no more effort.

The F.M.F.8 was in use for many years both at home and around the world, working on electric pylon work and other operations. It has only been in the past five years that these machines have been retired to be replaced by more modern versions. ■

Developed for Balfour Beatty, the 'F.M.F.8' Auto Winch Tractor

The rear view of the tractor with the anchor lowered ready for winching.

The finished article is testament to Terry's hard work.

Anniversary project

Terry Hanlon is proud that he restored a Power Major in its golden anniversary year

I have been interested in Fordson tractors since 1968 when, as a 15-year-old, I used to plough with a diesel Major and a Ransomes plough on my dad's farm at Dromome, Co Meath in Ireland.

After I finished schooling I went to England and spent five years in the Nottingham area where I ended up working for William West and Son as a diesel fitter before emigrating to Ft McMurray in Alberta, Canada, in 1976.

After four years as a mechanic I went into business for myself with a fellow Canadian. We had heavy equipment, bulldozers, diggers, motor graders etc and we contracted to oil companies to build their roads and pipelines. Over the following 26 years we had four companies, the last one being sold in 2006.

I had already bought a petrol Fordson Major at auction, which looked and sounded as good as the day it left the

factory in Dagenham, but now I had some time on my hands I decided to buy more Fordsons and start restoring them.

To date I have purchased 23 tractors, from the model F up to the Fordson Major 5000, among them a Fordson Power Major.

I bought this one in central British Columbia, a round trip of 1,800 kilometres and a day to drive there and a day home, which is kind of the norm in a country of this size.

Although the Power Major looked good, it was in need of a complete overall. I stripped it down to the rear axle housing, replacing bearings, seals, bushes and any part that was showing signs of 50 years of wear and tear.

This was my first major restoration and finding parts in Canada was difficult until I found a supplier in eastern Canada and also ordered from the UK.

I took apart the engine and had the machining on the block and crankshaft done locally. I also had the cylinder head and fuel pump and injector rebuilt in Edmonton.

Rebuild shops are limited in number

when you are dealing with a piece of equipment that's 50 years old. Some places I took these parts to had never heard of a Fordson Major so the challenge of rebuilding here is greater than in the UK.

After 18 months of sourcing parts and assembling them, the project started to take shape and the tractor looked like a Fordson Power Major again.

I had all the parts sand-blasted and painted with Endura paint, which is a two-pack product, and then put them back on the tractor.

Four new tyres were installed and it was ready for the big test. I filled it up with fluids and fired it up and it ran like a clock.

I must say I was pretty proud of restoring and preserving a piece of our agricultural heritage, especially on its 50th anniversary.

I certainly have lots of work ahead of me to get all the other models restored and running, but some day it will all come together. ■

Above: Removing the engine with a hoist.

Right: Having a cradle makes moving the transmission and rear axle much easier!

Above: The bare block; proving that this was a thorough restoration.

Left: Bull gears and differential.

Above: Terry with the rolling chassis back from the spray shop.

Above: The Major with the engine back on, awaiting the return of the side rails, wheels and tin work.

Highly desirable

The Super Dexta makes a good tractor for ploughing matches and has a good road speed, too.

Andrew Hall advises on what to look out for when buying a Super Dexta

During the 1950s the small tractor market was dominated by Ferguson (which was to become Massey Ferguson in 1958) and the Ford Motor Company in the UK had been concentrating on production of the Fordson Major. It only entered the small tractor market in late 1957 with the arrival of the Fordson Dexta.

The original Dexta was a development of the 9N and 8N ranges that were popular in the United States and much of the transmission followed a similar pattern to the previous models, albeit with six forward and two reverse gears rather than the four of the 8N.

The Dexta became a very popular machine and competed well with tractors like the Massey Ferguson 35, David Brown 880 and Nuffield Universal Three. Its production ran from 1957 to September 1964 when the new worldwide Ford range was launched.

During its production run the Dexta range underwent various improvements and increases of horsepower in line with other manufacturers. The last of the Dextas to be introduced was the New Performance model in June 1963 to give the Massey Ferguson 35X a run for its money, and this is the model featured in this buyer's guide.

These models were easily distinguished by the blue/grey colour scheme which became common on

all Ford tractor models thereafter.

If you decide to buy a Super Dexta, you will have a very desirable tractor that makes a good alternative to an MF 35 or similar. But, as with all tractors, they will have been used for all manner of tasks and will have wear and tear as a result. The following information should help ensure you spend your money wisely.

ENGINE

The engine is based on the Perkins P3 design and was built to Ford specification. The Super Dexta has a bore of 3.6 inches, compared with the earlier bore of 3.5 inches, which allowed for more power. The fuel system is Simms Minimec, which has an in-line pump with a centrifugal governor

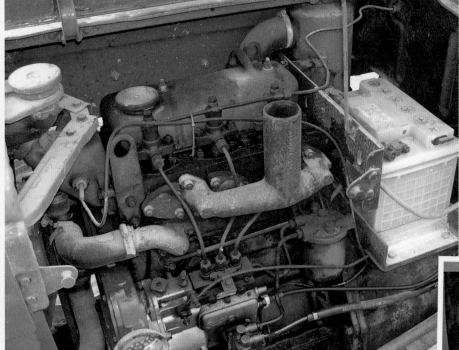

on the linkage. A pin may be located in one of two positions. One position prevents the clutch entering its second stage and is useful for loader work, but should not be used when operating pto-driven equipment. Clutch replacement involves splitting the tractor to access the clutch.

GEARBOX

The Dexta gearbox provides six forward and two reverse speeds and is mechanically robust. The most common problem is that of wear in the selectors, which allows the main gear lever to come out of its selector pocket. If this happens it is not too difficult to overcome by removing the four setscrews holding the cover plate and re-aligning the selectors before refitting

Above: Fuel tank is located at rear allowing for easy access to top of engine for servicing purposes.

Right: This left-hand view of the engine shows the Simms Minimec fuel pump.

providing smoother running than the earlier pneumatic-type used prior to April 1962.

The engines are mechanically reliable, consistent with other Perkins-based engines, and provided the oil has been kept clean and changed regularly should give many hours of service between overhauls.

When inspecting the engine it is good to check the cold starting performance. With the engine running check for any rattles or knocking from it – knocking may indicate badly-worn big end bearings and rumbling from the lower end may point to worn main bearings.

On high-hour machines expect some smoke from the exhaust, but this should clear as the engine picks up.

Oil leaks are not uncommon on harder-worked machines. This may leak from the rocker cover gasket and make the whole of the engine look worse than it really is, but is easy to cure. Also, the rear main oil seal is prone to leak and this is evident by the loss of oil through the bottom of the clutch housing. To cure this problem the tractor needs to be split at the clutch and the flywheel removed. The seal consists of two asbestos half-rings and is a bit of a fiddle to fit.

COOLING SYSTEM

The cooling system is much the same as on any other engine of its type. However, the cylinder block is vulnerable to cracking each side of the cylinders due to frost damage. Cracking may be evident behind the injector pump and below the camshaft housing on the right-hand side.

To prevent this occurring, and also to reduce the possibility of corrosion, it is good practice to keep the anti-freeze to

a good strength. Water pumps may leak also, but repair kits or complete pumps are available from many aftermarket stockists.

CLUTCH

Both a standard single-plate clutch or dual clutch providing live drive were available, although it is likely that a New Performance Dexta has the latter, as by the time this model arrived the benefits of live drive were well appreciated.

The clutches give no specific trouble in service provided they have been adjusted regularly and not 'ridden' by the operator. On live tractors the pedal has two positions

the levers. If this problem becomes too regular it is a good idea to have the levers built up at their ends to reduce the play.

A word of warning about starting Dextas. Make sure you are in the driving seat when operating the starter as it is easy to assume that the tractor is in neutral when in fact the gear lever has popped out of its socket. Otherwise, providing the oil has been maintained at the correct level the ▶

A right-hand view showing the point around the core plug which is vulnerable to frost damage.

The clutch linkage has two positions for the linkage. In the forward position the clutch will not enter second stage and is useful for loader work, but never for pto work!

gearbox should give good service. The oil level is checked by means of a level plug in the side of the transmission case and filled through a filler plug near the gear levers.

POWER TAKE-OFF

A standard 1⅜in diameter shaft is fitted to all Dextas and operated by a lever on the left-hand side of the transmission housing. Live drive models have a distinct advantage over standard models, as with all tractors. When inspecting, look for oil leaks around the shaft. This may indicate worn bearings but is easily remedied.

HYDRAULICS

The system used on all Dextas is a development of the Ford 8N and embodies both position and depth control. Ford called its depth control Qualitrol and a selector on the top right-hand side of the transmission casing selects either position or Qualitrol. There may also be a further flow control attached to the top cover together with an external services selector for tipping trailers etc.

The hydraulics are powered by a gear-type pump, which is located in the rear axle housing and draws oil from the axle separately from the gearbox.

The system is generally reliable but sometimes may fail due to problems associated with the linkage inside the housing. A common problem is that of the position control pin wearing out or breaking off and rendering the system inoperative. Standard linkage is category one but optional link arms with interchangeable ball ends were available.

BRAKES

The brakes on the Super Dexta are 14in drums operated by rods and shafts to provide independent brakes. These are adequate for their purpose if maintained correctly.

When inspecting the rear axle areas behind the brakes check for oil leaks from the axle housing. This may have contaminated the brakes

and reduced their efficiency.

Another thing to look for is seizure of the brakes and operating mechanism due to ingress of water or acids from manure where the tractor may have been used for yard scraping duties. In extreme cases the brake back plates may be corroded through and need replacement. This is not too difficult to perform but does affect the value of the tractor.

FRONT AXLE AND STEERING

Front axles are similar in style to Ferguson tractors and include a facility to adjust the track width. However, unlike the Ferguson which automatically maintains the toe-in adjustment, the Dexta requires the toe-in to be adjusted manually. There are scribed marks on the track arms and king pin housings to facilitate this.

Wear can take place in the king pins together with front wheel bearings and centre pivot. Parts to remedy this are available and the repairs are not too difficult.

The steering box is of worm and nut principle and is different from other steering box designs. The steering wheel is attached to the nut which sits inside the top of the column. The turning of the wheel acts upon a worm shaft which rises and descends for turning right and left respectively.

The whole steering box is lubricated through the nut that secures the steering wheel. This is often overlooked and, as a result, wear takes place between the worm shaft and nut. Badly worn boxes allow the steering wheel to wobble around with increased play.

Oil level must be maintained above the top of the worm shaft to provide necessary lubrication.

WHEELS AND TYRES

Wheels are pressed steel for both front and rear. Tyre sizes for front are 6.00-16 and 11.2-28 for the rear. Wheel rims should be checked for distortion and corrosion, particularly ex-scraper tractors, but are available new if necessary.

Above: The alternative to the drawbar is the pick-up hitch which works in conjunction with the three-point linkage. Here it is shown in the lowered position.

Inset: This tractor has the swinging drawbar which was common on earlier machines.

TIN WORK

This is fairly robust but there are areas of corrosion to watch for. Areas around the sides of the radiator cowl near to the top are prone to rusting through and the box sections and lower areas of the wings rust out due to mud collecting and retaining moisture. Fuel tanks do not escape corrosion either. They are flat-bottomed and have rust traps in the front lower corners.

Tin work availability is reasonable as front cowls and rear wings are available from various stockists. However, fuel tanks are not so easy to obtain and, if corroded, will either require repair or a second-hand replacement.

PRICES

Prices vary greatly according to condition. Tractors requiring much work may be obtained for under £1,000; machines in running order in ex-farm condition can fetch between £1,000 and £2,000. Restored examples, depending upon quality of finish and mechanical condition can fetch as much as £4,000, but one needs to ensure they are genuine machines.

SPARES

Due to increased interest in the model in recent years there is a healthy supply of spares available through a variety of suppliers such as Agriline (tel: 01527 579111), Dunlop Tractor Spares (tel: 02825 652560), Southern Counties Tractor Spares (tel: 01243 512109) and Bepco and Vapormatic through their nationwide stockists. ∎

Specification (New Performance models)

Fuel	Diesel
Cylinders	3
Bore/Stroke	3.6in x 5in
Capacity	2,500cc
Horsepower	44.5bhp @ 2,450rpm
Length overall	118.5in
Width (minimum track)	64.5in
Height (to top of steering wheel)	54.4in
Wheelbase	72.75in
Turning circle (using independent brakes)	18ft
Weight	3,165lb
Fuel tank capacity	7 gallons
Clutch	Standard tractors: 11in single plate Live-drive tractors: 9in dual plate
Transmission	6 forward, 2 reverse (alterations were made to ratios to improve performance)
Rear axle	Crown wheel and pinion Differential lock as standard
Brakes	14in drum
Power take-off	Live or standard pto 536rpm @ 1,550 engine rpm
Hydraulics	Three-point linkage with position and depth control Interchangeable category I and II ball ends available as an option

A right-hand view which demonstrates clearly the low profile of the Dexta and also the low centre of gravity making a safe tractor for work on slopes.

Thomas Bebb and his newly-restored 1958 Fordson Dexta.

Dexta challenge

Thomas Bebb from Melverley in Shropshire describes his first restoration

I have recently finished my first restoration. It was of a 1958 Fordson Dexta and has taken me two years and around £4,500 of hard-earned cash to complete. But it was totally worth it.

I am not mechanically-minded but, as the years go, by I seem to get better and that is why I wanted to restore a tractor – to teach myself more about tractor mechanics. I caught the restoration bug back in 2007 when I was at a local scrapyard where there were a lot of old tractors, some in reasonable condition and some that were just scrap. I took a fancy to a Dexta and so began looking for one, but to no avail. My dad asked a mate of his and he knew where there was one for sale just up in the

Dee Valley near Llangollen. We went and had a look the next day and at first I wasn't impressed. The Dexta was being used as a scraper tractor, there was hardly any oil on the dipstick and hardly any water in the radiator, but the owner had refurbished the gearbox and hydraulic systems.

We offered him a fair price but didn't hear from him for about three weeks when he rang up one evening and said I could have it for the agreed price. We went and picked it up a few days later.

For some reason someone had put a Super Dexta cowling on the front with lights on the side, so I checked the serial numbers which confirmed that it was a 1958 Dexta and not a Super.

On later inspection we realised that someone had driven the tractor into a pillar or something, because the left stabiliser bar

and steering arm were bent up and out. I made good progress for the first month or so in dismantling the Dexta, putting all the parts in little tubs and keeping all the different parts of the tractor together so that it would be easier to put back together. But as the weeks went on my budget went down and I couldn't buy all the parts at once, so many months went by before I could afford some parts, the first of which were the engine components.

Closer inspection of the engine was good: there was hardly any wear on the crank, the pistons were in good condition and the rings were still in a fair state so I just put new rings on and big end shells and a reconditioned cylinder head.

I then put the engine back and started it; it ran well, but it was surging terribly so I put a new diaphragm on and that made no

Above: Thomas washing the Dexta down after it arrived on the farm.

difference at all. However, I experimented with using a spare seal from the kingpin and now it only surges slightly when idling, but stops when in gear.

I then put on new brake shoes, pedal seals and pivot pin and rebushed the front axle and put in new wheel bearings.

The next job was the steering, which was very sloppy, but I bought a repair kit and did it up within a few hours.

The hardest job of the whole restoration was the painting. I knew that for the paint to stick successfully the castings needed to be rust-free, but I had heard stories of people who shot/sand-blasted their tractors and the steel or sand had entered the engine and wrecked it. To prevent this I bought a couple a tins of acid and spent days brushing the acid on the castings, and scraping them off.

After I'd stripped the paint, I bought some poly abrasive discs, which are like hard foam. They cost about £4 each and I used at least 20 of them, but they did a good job.

After this I steam-cleaned the Dexta and put two coats of red primer on with the airline. After leaving the primer to dry for at least a week I then painted on the blue with a brush; this took a lot of time but it filled in much of the pitting on the casting.

Much of the tin work was just scrap, the mudguards and footplates were far from rust-free but the bonnet was in reasonably good condition so I kept it.

After about 10 coats of blue, painted with the brush, I then put on an additional four coats of blue with the airline, including the tin work. This took out many of the streaks and covered parts I couldn't paint like behind the diesel pump and water pump. ■

After a coat or two of red oxide, the tractor looks much better.

Above: Applying the top coat.

Vintage and Classic Tractor Show, Shepton Mallet, Somerset, February 2008. Fordson Dexta industrial, capable of 30mph on the road. Laura achieved third prize in the 'Best Working Tractor' section.

First time out

Hobbies constantly need new blood. Joseph Lewis finds out what turned one young lady towards tractors

L aura Kimber, of Dorset, is the new owner of a 1962 Fordson Dexta Industrial. But why did she want one?

She explained: "My family has always been interested in vintage machines. Dad has several stationary engines, my brother loves steam trains and my uncle has two Fergie tractors, one petrol and one paraffin.

"We were taken to steam rallies when we were younger, but I wanted to do more than just look at them and joined a steam apprentice club, which gives young people the opportunity to learn to look after and drive traction engines.

"I enjoyed this for a few years and met my boyfriend, Chris, through driving his steam roller. We now rally his engine all across Dorset and he has helped me with my tractor endeavours."

Chris was also instrumental in the choice of tractor.

"I chose it because Chris knows a lot about Fordsons. His knowledge would be really useful during the restoration, especially in showing me what to do! The other reason was that I didn't want a huge tractor to begin with. I would rather start small and work my way up. "Finding my little Dexta was a bit of an accident. The rest of my family went to a local farm shop. They mentioned that the man who runs the shop was a keen collector, with two portable steam engines and several tractors. A few weekends later I went along to have a look, more out of curiosity than with any definite plans.

"I saw my Dexta with a 'for sale' sign on her, tucked away in a corner, looking rather forlorn. The rest, as they say, is history."

Once home, the new and exciting first tractor restoration began with an exciting discovery - "I did not realise quite how much fun an industrial Dexta would be when I bought her. She does about 30mph on the road, so I can go much further, much quicker, than most other Fordsons."

Working with Chris, Laura is learning as she goes and increasing her tractor knowledge every day.

"I have repaired the fuel tank (after pressure washing her and making the hole!), fitted lights, changed all the radiator hoses, fan belt, and wiring loom. We had the temperature gauge repaired and then this was re-fitted. A special moment came when we put in an ignition key!

"Some parts were too far gone so I obtained new replacements. It is easy to find the spare parts for Fordsons. I can sit at home in the warm and order them off the internet instead of hunting around for them all. I painted all the new bits I had bought for her, which included a new tool box and new badges.

"A recent incident made me feel like a true member of the tractor preservation world. Chris says that you can restore a tractor, but you do not really become a part of the movement until you have suffered your first breakdown. I 'became a part' when I learned to change the fuel filter on the side of the road!". ■

Above: Laura's Dexta at its first rally at Moorsvale County Park, pictured alongside Chris's 1901 Fowler D2 roller "Lord Kitchener".

Right: A sorry state with flat front tyre and no lights in the grille, but good back tyres and original Crimble of Staines supplier plates. A good basis for restoration.

A rear view emphasises the good rear tyres and the sound tin work. The industrial nature is yet to be revealed. Note the absence of hydraulics, with a blanking plate, where the hydraulics should be. Photographs: Laura Kimber.

Never-ending story

This Dexta just goes on and on, Chris McCullough discovers

Fordson Dexta tractors were very popular little workhorses in their day and can still be found in high numbers around Northern Ireland farms.

From the 1960s and right through the peak years of agricultural mechanisation the Dexta helped develop farming – pretty much to the same extent as the Ferguson, although it was not recognised for it.

You can be sure to see a variety of Dextas at any rally or road run, most of them enhanced by restorers to their former glory; but what about those that still have to work for a living?

Alan Coulter, who runs a dairy farm in Ballinamallard, County Fermanagh, Northern Ireland, has one

such Dexta that earns its keep.

His was manufactured in 1962 and bought brand-new by his late father Fred for the princely sum of £750.

However, this Dexta does not have an easy life. It has had to work hard in County Fermanagh's tough conditions and it has clocked up more than 10,000 hours on... well... a few clocks, if truth be known.

Alan said: "The first clock stopped working at 5,200 hours and the next one stopped at 5,300 hours, so I know she has over 10,000 hours service carried out for us.

"She never lets us down, but has had the engine overhauled on occasion with the normal service and maintenance. We run a dairy and beef farm here so you can imagine all the little chores that need to be done - the Dexta is almost always the first one started to carry out these tasks."

Indeed, Alan uses his Dexta to sow fertiliser on the challenging Fermanagh grasslands and, when the sower is unhooked, the linkbox goes on. With it, Alan says, any job – whether it be fencing or feeding cattle – can be done with his reliable Dexta.

Alan's tractor is fitted with a cab but, as he admits, this was a later addition to help deal with the wet Northern Ireland weather.

As most Dexta drivers know, these models can – and usually do – stick in gear when you least expect it. And then the arduous task begins of unscrewing the gearsticks to fight blind with the gear 'knuckles' to free them up again.

However, Alan's Dexta seems to be free of this fault. "Yes, I have heard many Dexta drivers complaining about this but I think it depends on the pilot whether this happens or not," he laughed. ∎

A Family affair

A teenager learns the ropes with a bit of help, writes Michael Mullen

ichael Stainton may only be 16 but he is already an experienced restorer of classic tractors and his 1964 Fordson New Performance Super Dexta was awarded the 'Best Fordson' prize at summer's Cumbria Steam Gathering at Flookburgh.

The hobby is very much a family affair with his father George having been a tractor enthusiast all his life and Michael remembering sitting on his uncle's 1951 Ferguson TEA when he was just three years old. Now the family has an extensive tractor collection at home in Cumbria.

It was in 2006 that the team acquired the Dexta from a Lancashire tractor dealer. It had had quite a hard life, but the engine was good and the transmission was sound,

so the basis of the project was there.

The engine was fully serviced with injectors, oils and filters and the like - the tractor is fitted with a 44.5hp three-cylinder engine and uprated Simms Minimec pump with mechanical governor and, although the Super Dexta has more power than the earlier examples, it is slower for some reason on the road. Perhaps it is all down to the governor as the Super Dexta is classed as a 19.53mph machine and the earlier ones are supposed to be only capable of 16.8mph, although Ford apprentice Frank Summerlin concludes that the proofmeter was none-too-accurate on the Dexta, so you can get misled.

The dual clutch proved a problem for the father and son and they had the tractor split three times before they had the mechanism right. They used parts from various suppliers and some of the parts were not perfect

so do check that the new items are right before fitting them or you might end up doing the job three times, as in this case.

The steering was given the full works, particularly the steering box, which is not the best in the first place (especially the top bearing). Repair is not easy but critical in any Dexta restoration. Michael replaced the track rod ends, the rubber covers on all the joints and the grease nipples. Bearings, king pins and the centre pin went on.

The hydraulics needed some work and always need to be checked out as they can be a problem on the Dexta, particularly in the flow control-type system on the Super Dexta. Michael and George stripped down the power lift unloading valve, replaced the O-rings and spring in the valve, and more. It was re-assembled and has not been any problem since. The lift arms ▶

Above left: The Simms Minnimec pump and mechanical governor were all part of the Super Dexta.

Above Right: The six-speed high and low levers are seen, as is the radius arm bracket.

Top of page: Making sure the badge fits correctly to the front panel is something to be done before painting takes place.

Left: Good steering is very important on a Dexta.

and linkage were replaced and rebushed where required. With the drums removed the brakes were relined and the handbrake ratchet was also sorted out. In fact, the brakes are very positive on the Super Dexta.

A new original battery box was found on a stall at a show to replace the original, which was corroded right through. Michael stripped the dynamo and starter down and, with new brushes and a good clean, they now work perfectly. George put a new control box on with a good quality battery and the wiring loom was authentically

you can get misled - as George has found.) After finishing the paintwork, the tyres were carefully blown up in a cage before being re-assembled on the tractor with new wheel nuts.

The tractor was ready for the rally field in August 2006 but it was to be two years later at the same show that it was to take first prize in its class. By carefully rebuilding it, the father and son have made sure it has stood the test of time - and perhaps looks better now than when it first came out two years ago.

When asked his ambition for the future, Michael indicated it might be in welding and fabrication, but in the tractor line it's got to be a Roadless Fordson Dexta 4x4. Only time will tell, but it looks as though Michael is going places in tractor restoration thanks to his family's support. That's what families are all about - working together. rebraided with cloth which came from a vintage car supplier as the wires were very good.

A second-hand steering wheel was obtained and all-new gauges went on

during the process. The lights were all cleaned and re-used and, instead of renickeling the lens back plates they were wire-wooled, repainted with chrome look-alike paint and are the "bees' knees," according to George.

Michael has become an ace welder over the years; new foot plates and a seat went on, besides other sundry repairs

The wings were original, but the front grille panel had the works and a new Super Dexta badge came from Bertie Dunlop in Northern Ireland.

being carried out along the way. The wings were original, but the front grille panel had the works and a new Super Dexta badge came from Bertie Dunlop in Northern Ireland. It fitted perfectly to the right contour - there shouldn't be a gap at the top between the long badge and the front grille; this is something that can lose marks in competitions and, if there is a gap, it needs to be sorted before painting.

All the paintwork was wire-brushed, not sand-blasted, and primered with good

anticorrosive paints. George and Michael spray the paintwork outside in the yard which means they had lots of rubbing down to do, particularly to get the dust and flies out of the paintwork, and they added a touch of yacht varnish to the final coat, which certainly gives their paintwork an edge.

It was possible to use the original wheels and these were wire-brushed and primered before the new Goodyear 12.4/11-28 tyres went on the rear and 600 x 16 on the front.

After checking them out the tyres were let down and lining sheets placed around and inside the rim before spraying top coat Ford grey on. (There are three shades of grey so make sure you have the right one. If you are not sure try and match it to some original paint, but make sure you polish the paint before matching it to the colour chips as a very complete back end with pto shaft cover and decals all in the right place.

The wings were original, but the front grille panel had the works and a new Super Dexta badge came from Bertie Dunlop in Northern Ireland. ■

Half track: full resto

A rare 1964 tractor gets the treatment, as Peter Squires reports

The columns of *T&M* provided John Hall with the chance to buy a Fordson Dexta half-track - "it had seen work in the forests and, although the tin work had a bit of a battering, it was totally original," he said.

His tractors – he has three more Fordsons at home - are restored to a very high standard, but all do what they were meant to do and that's work!

On its arrival at his home in Derbyshire John began a closer inspection of the tractor (s/n 09D 927252) and discovered that the engine needed a rebuild, the tin work was well worn and battered but in rot-free condition, while the half-tracks were complete.

He started with the engine. On the bottom end, the main bearings had run with water in the oil, causing the white metal to peel out of the centre of two of the big end shells.

"Luckily it hadn't scored the crank, so I just fitted new big end bearings," John said.

At the top end, new rings were fitted as number two and three compression rings were all broken up. A valve guide had also broken, so he had the head skimmed and the valves were reseated and installed.

When the engine was refitted and started up, the tractor was given a test drive before work restarted on the rest of it.

The front axle was OK, but John fitted a replacement steering box as the original was beyond repair. The starter motor, dynamo and injectors were all removed and given a full reconditioning before being refitted. A new radiator had already been fitted and the gearbox and hydraulic system proved to be working well.

The tin work was stripped next. John, a central heating engineer by trade, stripped and sandblasted the cowl and bonnet to see how damaged they were under the rust.

The wings were just too far gone and John

had to settle for a new pair. The cowl was badly battered but, with plenty of patience and a lot of hammer-work, he brought it back very close to its former glory.

"The tractor was never meant to be a 'concours' show model when restored. I believe if it works, leave it alone," John said. "I also believe if a tractor is restored, it should look something similar to when it came out of the factory.

"If you look closely you can still see slight dents in the cowl, but does it really matter? I'm pleased with how my tractors look and they are all still working. Those bumps are part of the tractor's past, probably gained whilst working in the Welsh forests."

The wheels were removed and given the sandblast treatment before painting. The half-tracks were complete and in reasonable condition.

Replacement seals were fitted to the power rams and holes were cut in the wings to take the hydraulic hoses through to

The half tracks certainly give John's half-track extra grip in the waterlogged ground.

the rams. The steel pipes from the control box to the rams were also renewed.

New grilles for the cowl were bought as the originals had long gone. One headlamp was still fitted to the Dexta and just needed a new reflector. The other headlamp was too far gone. John made two sidelights from scratch and added a new temperature gauge.

His plan was to work the Dexta with his Browns' mole plough at a depth of around 18in to drain the field beside his bungalow, the tracks giving extra grip on the waterlogged land.

It is all grass, sloping into a 'swilly' before rising up again. The soil held

the rainwater, making it very slow draining, half the field being clay.

The Dexta completed its task with ease; a good five feet of track were on the ground, giving more than enough adhesion.

In the corner of the field, four to five inch-diameter roots of some old silver birch trees were still just below the ground but the half-tracks did their job, providing the little Dexta with extra grip on the slippery ground and the roots were pulled out like rotten teeth.

"Without the half-track Dexta, they would certainly still be there, as an ordinary Dexta would just have slid in the wet ground," John admitted, adding with a smile: "It did rear up once or twice though!" ∎

The hydraulic system for raising and lowering the half-track rams.

Taking shape. Note the tyre valve protectors, proof of a working life in the forests!

Aboard a Doe

Dave Beare test drives the big one, the legendary Triple D

Ernie Doe's production of tandem Fordson Majors in the late 1950s resulted from a small but persistent need for serious power and traction to pull multi-share ploughs through heavy soils such as those in Essex and Lincolnshire.

The design was originated by Essex farmer George Prior, who wanted around 100bhp and four-wheel drive, but could find nothing suitable on the market. Today 100bhp-plus 4x4 tractors are commonplace but 50 years ago nothing of the kind existed.

George Prior's tandem tractor was a sensation and Ernie Doe soon became involved as his company was the local Fordson dealership and probably supplied many of the parts that Prior used.

The original George Prior tractor needed a fair amount of re-engineering before it could be sold commercially since few of the controls were linked. For instance, changing gear on the

front unit necessitated dismounting and using the original gear lever at the front, then remounting to drive off.

Doe was already producing a number of Fordson conversions and soon developed the necessary linked controls and improved some of the more rudimentary aspects of the Prior tractor.

The Triple D, as it became known, was unique in 1958 in having 104bhp, tremendous traction and amazing manoeuvrability for its size. Despite being 19ft 9ins long the central articulation was nearly 90 degrees, enabling a Triple D to turn virtually in its own length. At about 21 feet, the turning circle was five feet less than a standard Fordson Major.

It was, however, rather more complicated to drive as front and rear units still had some separate controls and drivers occasionally came to grief from lack of experience. It was also rather expensive and £2,350 for a Super Triple D was big money for a tractor in the early 1960s.

This was rather less than a crawler capable

of similar performance on heavy soil, such as a weighty 90bhp Caterpillar which would have cost over £7,000, but a Doe was no lightweight, tipping the scales at 4.5 tonnes.

George Prior and Ernie Doe's tractor was an instant success and around 350 were made between 1958 and 1964, being exported all over the world.

A replacement, the 130bhp Doe 130, was introduced in 1965 and followed the same principles but used two more modern Ford 5000 skid-units. Progress soon caught up however; mainstream manufacturers brought out their own 4x4 high-power tractors and economies of scale meant they were able to undercut the Doe 130 on price. Within a few years Doe production ceased and the family business reverted to selling Ford tractors, an activity continued to this day by Ernest Doe's grandson, Colin Doe.

Triple Ds were virtually hand-made on the Doe workshop floor. Large lumps of tractor were bought in from Ford, then modified in the welding and machine shops, using wherever possible readily-available

AAS189

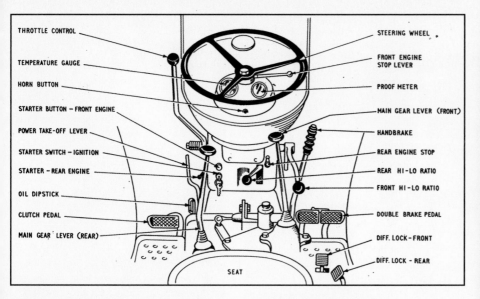

View from the driving seat- a lot more controls than on a standard Fordson Major.

parts such as the four steering-rams which originated from Horndraulic loaders.

The centre turntable, with its four steering rams, was a stroke of genius. It allowed near-90 degree articulation whereas, with only two rams, a Triple D would have had a huge turning circle and been cumbersome, unwieldy and unsuccessful.

Steering on a Triple D is purely hydraulic; pressure is provided by a pump driven from the front crank pulley of the rear engine and supplied to a shuttle-valve connected to the steering wheel which operates two rams each side.

Gearing is high and, to anyone used to a normal Fordson Major, steering is feather-light and very direct.

The standard Fordson clutch pedal of the rear unit is connected hydraulically via a balance-bar to two master and slave cylinders operating clutches in both units. Gear and ratio changing of the front unit is also achieved hydraulically.

Two additional gear levers are fitted to the right side of the driver's seat, one controlling high/low ratios and

the other main gear changing.

A series of small Lockheed hydraulic master cylinders transmits fore/aft and side-to-side motion from the rear-mounted lever to the front unit, where a steel box sits on top of what would be a Fordson gear lever. A further series of identical hydraulic cylinders, attached to this, replicates motion from the rear lever to the front gearbox. The two gearboxes are independently controlled so careful thought is needed before changing gear. The one thing not to do on a Doe is to end up with the front unit in reverse and the rear unit in first - a massive self-destruct follows!

It was quite common in use, however, to run the front unit in a higher forward gear than the rear to aid traction.

A new throttle control lever is mounted to the left of the steering wheel, which links both front and rear engines. They can be synchronised by adjusting link-rods, while the old Fordson throttle lever on the right side of the instrument binnacle now serves as the front engine stop-lever. All this sounds very complicated but in practice ▶

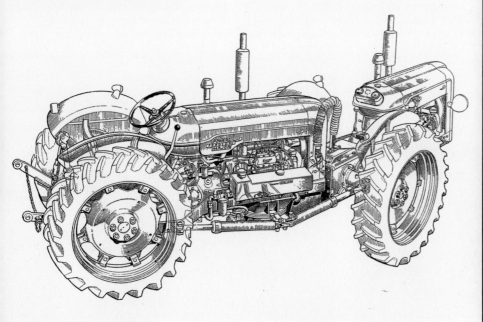

Drawing of the first Doe Triple D.

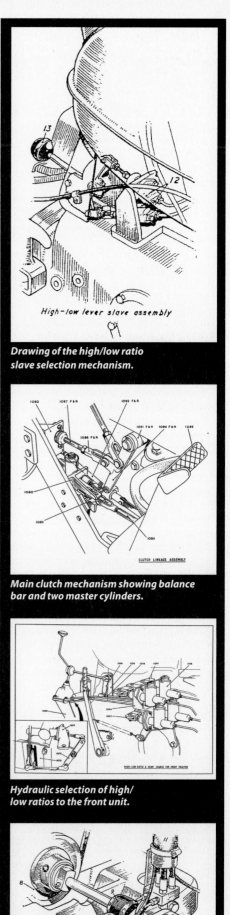

Drawing of the high/low ratio slave selection mechanism.

Main clutch mechanism showing balance bar and two master cylinders.

Hydraulic selection of high/low ratios to the front unit.

Hydraulic pump and drive shaft driven from front pulley of rear engine.

Ray Leach goes into a tight turn…..

On full-lock the driver can almost touch the front unit.

it works well and with practice driving a Doe would become second-nature.

Enough of the technicalities: what is it like to drive?

I was given cockpit drill by Ray Leach, owner of a magnificent 1959 Doe Triple D tractor that has been seen in action at many shows around Wales over the past few years, before he let me loose in a large field on the Llandysul showground. First impression - the front unit radiator surround is a looooong way away!

Both engines fire up instantly and tick over quietly; first gear of the front unit is engaged before the rear. Ray recommends lifting the clutch pedal gently until the front unit can just be felt pulling to ensure it is in gear. The clutch pedal is then dipped again and the rear gearlever slotted into the same gear as the front. A few hundred rpm are added with the linked throttle control lever, the clutch pedal gently eased up and off we go.

It's immediately apparent that the steering has no feel whatsoever and is highly power-assisted. Any slight movement of the wheel and the vehicle reacts instantly: the front unit swings

disconcertingly quickly and the first 20 yards are travelled in a series of long swerves.

Once one is accustomed to such instant changes of direction, the Triple D is straightforward to drive although the proper sequence of gear-changing needs to be borne in mind at all times.

Turning on full lock is a revelation. It doesn't seem possible that such a long machine can turn within its own length but it can and the driver finds himself grinning from ear to ear as the front unit moves alongside him. One can only imagine what it must be like using a five or six-furrow plough behind a Triple D with all that power and traction. No doubt this is why any Doe bought in for preservation has absolutely had it: they were all worked to death!

Ray's Doe Triple D was delivered new to Lloyd Jenkins, of The Lodge, South Braithwaite, near Doncaster in South Yorkshire. It spent a few years ploughing the big arable fields of the area but was subsequently sold to an unknown ploughing contractor on February 17, 1961. From then on it worked long and hard until, thoroughly worn out, it was returned to Essex in the late

1990s as a virtual wreck, ripe for restoration.

Ray bought it as an unfinished project, has been working on it ever since and continues to do so. The quality of his restoration is superb and it was a real privilege to be allowed to drive a Doe - it was a day to remember. ∎

View of a Triple D from the driver's seat - two bonnets and two exhausts.

Ray's Triple D approaches full articulation at Orllwyn Teifi in August 2006.

Designer Dextas

Dave Beare finds out what can be done to these icons

Graham Morris is not only a Fordson Dexta man through-and-through; he also builds very effective four-wheel drive conversions of these versatile small tractors.

He first became involved with 4WD tractors when he bought a Roadless-converted Ford 3000 with a front crown wheel missing several teeth (the axle being from Selene of Italy) and found that replacement parts would cost £1,800!

A much-modified Land Rover axle was substituted with success and Graham then adapted this technology to convert a P3-powered Ferguson TEA-20, an MF 35 and a couple of Fordson Dextas.

He certainly knows a thing or two about this last model as he owns a dozen of them which work constantly on the farm at Cwmbach.

Dextas were produced between 1957 and 1964 and designed to give the Ford Motor Company something to sell in competition with Harry Ferguson's hugely-successful TE-20 and MF 35 series tractors.

Ford hated the idea of a category in which it had nothing to offer customers and was especially disgruntled by Ferguson since it regarded TE-20 tractors as little more than a rip-off of the Ford-Ferguson 9N and 2N, which were made between 1939 and 1947. The Ferguson had Harry Ferguson's patented and now-universal three-point hydraulic linkage, the subject of much litigation between the two companies in the 1950s.

So the Fordson Dexta was aimed squarely at Harry Ferguson's backyard and was commercially successful, although it never did get as close to farmers' wallets or affections as the proverbial Little Grey Fergie.

A Dexta's power was supplied by Ford's version of the world-famous Perkins 152 three-cylinder diesel with ▶

Dave tests the Tandem Tractor – very easy to drive once you know which lever does what!

32hp, although a few petrol-engined Dextas were made, as we shall see.

Graham Morris's business, All-Grip Traction, is run in partnership with his son David and has now carried out a good number of 4WD conversions, which have proved so successful that one customer, who had an MF 35 converted some years ago, has given them an MF 65 to turn into a 4x4.

All-Grip Traction-converted tractors have the front axle driven from a power take-off sandwich plate fitted between the gearbox and final-drive sub-assemblies, which encloses a wide Morse chain taking power to the front propshaft. Chains are very tough and easily adaptable to different installations, as well as being almost silent in operation.

All-Grip Traction's original Dexta 4x4 used a Land Rover front axle which normally has the diff offset on the right but the firm's first customer was a champion ploughman, Andrew Hewitt, who found the diff and propshaft were in his line of sight for ploughing.

To solve the problem the sandwich plate was turned round with the output on the left, the Land Rover axle was inverted and the crown wheel moved to the other side of the pinion.

Graham has recently bought this Dexta 4x4 back from Andrew and has several

Creators of the Tandem Tractor – Andy Belfield left, Graham Morris centre and David Morris right.

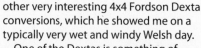

other very interesting 4x4 Fordson Dexta conversions, which he showed me on a typically very wet and windy Welsh day.

One of the Dextas is something of a rarity, a 1963 Roadless Super Dexta with a Selene front axle, one of only 23 ever made. Technically, it is very similar to other Roadless conversions though naturally somewhat smaller and lighter than the company's usual offerings.

Then we saw something completely unfamiliar, a 'Super' Super Dexta 4WD reminiscent of a miniaturised Muir-Hill, with overshot bonnet and an unusually long engine.

Graham and fellow-engineer Andy Belfield built this machine from a spare Dexta "to see if we could."

It features an 88hp six-cylinder version of the Perkins P3/152 three-cylinder engine which was used in Allis-Chalmers' combine harvesters. The 'Super' Super Dexta is fitted with All-Grip Traction's power take-off to the front axle, but with an added feature, the nose section of a Land Rover transfer box, enabling drive to the front axle to be disconnected.

Andy Belfield had to fabricate an engine frame and very complex stepped aluminium sump to enable the engine to sit astride the axle. I briefly drove this tractor and it pulls like a train, although the steering is fairly heavy.

Now we come to the most fantastic Dexta of all – the Belfield Tandem Tractor made by Andy Belfield for Graham Morris. It's a miniature Doe Triple-D made from two Dextas.

It took an extraordinary amount of head-scratching, designing and fabrication to make the Tandem work properly and, as a result, it is beautifully engineered. Like a real Triple-D everything is controlled from the driver's seat on the rear unit, from starting both engines, disengaging clutches, engaging gears, steering and accelerators. ▶

Above: Andy Belfield goes into a tight turn as puts the wonderfully-fabricated, tandem Super Dexta through its paces.

markets: no petrol Dextas seem to have been offered as production tractors.

The engine is instantly recognisable as a Standard-built Ferguson-type four-cylinder unit but there are differences, the cylinder-block is a different casting, made to mate up to the Fordson Dexta transmission. Alongside is a rather dilapidated Dexta with a special 12-speed transmission, housed in a sandwich plate and built by Rotary Hoes specifically for

market gardeners, with a very low crawler gear designed for rotovating. Graham came across this tractor by accident, while out buying Massey Ferguson parts! These things happen, as we all know.

* Graham and David Morris can be contacted at All-Grip Traction, Henllys Farm, Cwnbach, Builth Wells LD2 3RW (01982 553791 or 07971 356970) and Andy Belfield at Belfield Engineering, Llandrindod Wells (01597 823992). ■

Above: Central articulation of the Tandem using dumper components.

The foundation of this amazing machine is a turntable from an articulated dumper truck with twin hydrostatic-drive steering rams each side. In a brief field test the steering was found to be ultra-light and very responsive but, unlike a real Triple-D, not too high a ratio, so it was very easy indeed to drive.

We plan to carry a more in-depth look at the Tandem Tractor in another issue.

Elsewhere in Graham's collection there's a fine restored standard Dexta with just 1,100 hours from new on the clock, an unusual narrow vineyard Dexta modified by Stormont Engineering for the French market, and then an almost-mythical petrol-engined Dexta.

Very few were ever made, possibly only prototypes which were assessed for Nordic

There are very low hours from new on this Dexta, just 1,100.

The rear unit of D330 in the 'Malcolm Beaton' auction - turntable and rams on the floor!

Easy does it

Peter Squires sees a DDD being reborn

After the hammer went down on a Triple D at Cheffins 'Malcolm Beaton' auction last November, the machine left for Nottinghamshire - but didn't look much like a Triple D at all.

At some stage it had been split and rebuilt as two separate 1963 Super Majors (as many were). It still had its Ernest Doe supplier badges and the cutaway in the front weight where the hydraulic pump drive once sat.

But that was about it!

The lot comprised the rear tractor with its original turntable, rams, three out of the four serial number plates, bonnet and patent plates - the original rear half of Triple D D330.

It was knocked down to Bernard Saunders from Farnsfield in Nottinghamshire, who had been driving James Hardstaff's blue-grey Triple D last year and caught the Dual Power bug.

On arrival in Nottinghamshire the first job was to locate another 1963 Super Major

to be the front half of the tractor. It was taken to John Hayward's workshop for assessment before restoration began.

Donor tractors were needed; these and other components came from Richard Fenton, Ben Craig, Miles Hardy and Ford and Fordson Association chairman Peter Godwin.

The original turntable was in a mess. It had seen previous use as a turntable on a trailer's front axle and was well-worn. The bottom plate was salvageable but the top plate, which fitted via a cradle to the rear tractor's side-frames, was past restoring. The centre plate, from where the steering rams fitted, was also beyond repair. The rams needed restoring and a Vickers Vane hydraulic pump used to power the rams needed sourcing.

Allan Henshaw-Allcock took both engines into his workshop for examination and restoration as John Hayward began to sort and lay out the parts needed.

DT Stone Engineering, of Pinxton in Nottinghamshire, took on the task of repairing and machining the turntable plates and rams, while John stripped and rebuilt

the gearboxes from the donor front tractors.

That was not a simple task, however. Of the donor tractors the most suitable one had a different gearbox ratio - there are three different ratios for the Majors (before serial number 08C 960337, after 08C 960337 and an optional 3.5 to 1 crown wheel and pinion) – so John had to mix and match the gearboxes until he had the right one to match the rear unit.

Once Allan had restored the two engines and John had assembled the forward gearbox and other components it was time to start making both units look like a Triple D again.

Richard Esam Welding and Fabrications of Oxton, Nottinghamshire, (07814 976143) profile-cut the centre and the top turntable plates along with the support cradle and tube for the phosphor-bronze bush.

The turntable top plate is welded into in a 'saddle' that fits to the rear tractor's side-frames. This also incorporates the long phosphor-bronze bush where the front tractor's steel pivot shaft locates. ▶

Above: Accurate measuring by John makes sure the turntable saddle is welded perfectly in place.

Right: John Hayward (left) and Nick Key line up the rear unit's side-frames.

Due to welding distortion on the outer steel tube the phosphor-bronze bush inside had to be line-bored (around 25 thou) to bring it back onto centre-line.

This was carried out by Rhodes Waterhouse and, once married up to the pivot pin, the front axle was removed and the Doe was definitely looking more ship-shape!

Nick Key and John Hayward cut and drilled the heavy-duty side-frames for the rear unit from 15mm steel plate, which was thicker than the original Doe plating of 0.5in. John had kept the patterns and

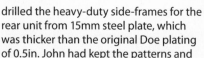

John had kept the patterns and measurments from building his own Triple-D, so this was a time-saver.

measurements from building his own Triple D, so this was a time-saver.

Once all the plates had been cut and checked against the rear tractor, Nick Key set about weld-tacking, before completing some very neat runs of weld.

As January ended D330 was looking

a lot different than it did two months before when the hammer came down on what looked like a basic Fordson Major.

Bernard hopes the machine will be ready for the annual Newark & Notts Agricultural Show in Spring, but there's still a long way to go.

* The Doe's original owners were William, Grace and Michael Chaddock from Glastonbury. The second owner is shown on the buff logbook as Michael Chaddock. Looking in Stuart Gibbard's Ford Tractor Conversions book, Somerset only had one Triple D and it looks certain this is it.

Above: The three-plate turntable in position. Note the lugs on the centre-plate for the steering rams.

Left: John inspects the rear frame before it is lifted into position.

Nick gently slides the primary gearbox into the gearbox housing as John checks the opposite end.

THE DOE GROWS

Bernard and his team are tackling the gearbox. You'd think it would be simple enough to get a second Major and couple it up to the first; but no!

There are three different gearbox ratios for a Major. When they are working, both units will be put in the same gear but if the gearbox ratios are different, one unit will try and move faster than the other.

Ratios are basically determined by the diameter of the gearwheels and the number of teeth per gearwheel. The three ratios are shown (left/right/above/below)

The ratio is stamped (but not always) on the front transmission housing mating flange where it mates to the gearbox flange and is usually un-noticeable as it's hidden under a good thickness of paint.

John Hayward, in whose workshop Bernard's DDD is being assessed, noticed the different ratios once the front transmission housings had been sand-blasted. As he had a handful of donor gearboxes on site, the plan was for a stripdown followed by a 'pick & mix' until the correct ratios could be found and built-up.

CROWN AND PINION GEARS.

The pinion gear takes the drive from the engine and gearbox centre line and turns it by 90° to the crown gear which rotates the bull gears, finally turning the tractor wheels.

The pinion on Bernard's rear Doe unit had 10 teeth but John noticed the crown for the front unit had 8

teeth, so this had to be changed for another 10 tooth pinion gear!

With the main gearbox, the main lower shaft gear had 34 teeth, but one of the donor gearboxes had a slightly smaller diameter gear, even though both had 34 teeth. The top shaft gear had 11 teeth and this needed to be replaced by a gear with 13 teeth in order to mesh correctly and give the correct ratio.

The primary gearbox sits inside the front transmission housing and consists of two gear shafts (upper and lower). Included is the gear wheel to drive on to the pto shaft, the bevel gear for a belt pulley drive, the selectors to change from the high to low speed ratio and the handbrake plate assembly.

Once John and his colleague Nick Key, ▶

Above: The primary gearbox with the main lower shaft pinion marked 'A' and the primary upper shaft gear marked 'B'.

The eight-toothed pinion bevel gear was changed for a 10-tooth gear.

Looking through the gearbox housing inspection hole at the primary upper shaft. Label 'A' indicates the low gear, 'B' the main upper gear and 'C' the transmission main drive gear.

Above: The main gearbox shafts. 'A' reverse pinion slides into the lower shaft gear, 'B' is where the gearshift forks fit, 'C' are the roller bearings and 'D' is the ball bearing that was changed.

Above: Looking inside the standard ratio primary gearbox. Marked in blue are the shift fork positions for hi-low gear ratios.

had removed the necessary components, four long locating dowels were swapped with four of the primary gearbox bolts. This would make removing and relocating the primary gearbox easier as it has to be removed horizontally out of the transmission housing.

BALLS AND ROLLERS

Another problem encountered when refitting the correct ratio gears was that of the bearings that supported the gear shafts. The originals were roller bearings and, as well as being able to rotate around the shaft, they had a degree of lateral movement along it.

The replacement bearings were ball bearings, having no lateral movement and a tighter fit into the cups. This lack of movement meant that the gears were almost impossible to select via the main gear stick. This was cured by replacing

the ball bearings with roller-types.

Before refitting the gearbox, a gasket was cut using the gearbox flange as a template. The mating face inside the transmission housing was cleaned and Nick added a little gasket sealant before offering up the gasket and sliding it along the locating studs into position.

Take note that at the bottom of the transmission mating face there is a crescent cut-away and this must also be removed from the gasket! Nick did this with a small ball pein hammer when the gasket was in place. Once he was happy, a little more sealant was added to the outer face of the gasket and the gearbox face was cleaned.

Nick and John guided the gearbox on to the four locating studs and the gearbox was slid into position.

As the gearbox slid further into place

John could keep an eye on things and feed the roller bearings into their cups as the shafts approached. As the gearbox main lower shaft pinion located into the front transmission housing a little bit of levering was needed but the teeth on this shaft soon interlocked with its counterpart as the needle bearings slid into their cups.

Nick held the gearbox tight to the transmission while John offered up and tightened two more bolts. Once this was done the locating bolts could be removed one at a time, replacing each with a securing bolt.

Once John and Nick were happy that all the gears could be selected, another inspection was carried out. At this point no oil was added, as a lot more work would be carried out before the inspection plates were fitted to the outside of the front transmission housing. ▶

Gear	Ratios		Speed (mph) at 1200rpm
	Gearbox	Overall	
1st	6.62:1	123.1:1	1.56
2nd	4.70:1	87.3:1	2.19
3rd	3.68:1	68.4:1	2.80
4th	2.615:1	48.6:1	3.94
5th	1.875:1	34.8:1	5.49
6th	1.043:1	19.3:1	9.87
High ratio	2.73:1	50.7:1	3.77
Low ratio	4.91:1	91.1:1	2.10

Tractors before serial number 08C 960337.

Gear	Ratios		Speed (mph) at 1200rpm
	Gearbox	Overall	
1st	7.82:1	182.0:1	1.058
2nd	6.04:1	140.2:1	1.362
3rd	4.00:1	92.88:1	2.061
4th	3.09:1	71.65:1	2.67
5th	1.875:1	43.54:1	4.38
6th	0.958:1	22.25:1	8.61
High ratio	2.96:1	68.60:1	2.781
Low ratio	5.79:1	134.50:1	1.425

Tractors from serial number 08C 960337 with 4.375 to 1 Crown Wheel & Pinion.

Gear	Ratios		Speed (mph) at 1200rpm
	Gearbox	Overall	
1st	7.82	145.6:1	1.32
2nd	6.04	112.10:1	1.70
3rd	4.00	74.30:1	2.578
4th	3.09	57.32:1	3.338
5th	1.875	34.83:1	5.48
6th	0.958	17.80:1	10.75
High ratio	2.96	54.88:1	3.478
Low ratio	5.79	107.60:1	1.778

Tractors from serial number 08C 960337 with optional 3.5 to 1 Crown Wheel & Pinion.

Gary Barnard (seated) with Roy and Allan Henshaw-Allcock check the hydraulics as the Doe arrives at Bilsthorpe.

SLAVES LABOUR

For the hydraulic steering system, oil is stored in a separate tank on the rear unit. A vane pump is fitted to this unit, being rotated by a driveshaft from the rear unit's front pulley. The vane pump increases the flow rate to an average of 10 gallons per minute to the system. The standard Super Major hydraulics have a flow rate of around five gallons per minute to operate the rear lift arms and accessories such as a tipping trailer ram or front loader when fitted.

With the Triple Doe needing constant steering, the additional hydraulic system gives more power to the machine.

Four single-acting rams control the direction of the Triple Doe, two on either side, working in pairs. The vane pump delivers the oil to a valve with two exit ports, one each for both of the master rams. As the steering wheel is turned, a valve opens up one port to allow oil into the master ram for the direction needed. As the steering wheel is turned in the opposite direction, the valve closes and its opposite is opened, forcing oil into the opposite master ram, and the front unit changes direction.

The flow valve has a 'flow reducing tap' (shown right) fitted to throttle down the front unit's turn-rate.

A compensating ram is fitted to the underbelly of the rear unit. On a standard tractor, as the steering wheel is turned the road wheels turn. Stop steering and the road wheels stop turning. On the Triple-D, turn the steering wheel and rods operate from the steering arm to operate the flow valve which supplies the steering rams with oil and the front unit turns. Once the flow valve opens, the flow is constant. This would result in the front unit trying to turn permanently until the steering wheel was turned in the opposite direction.

With the compensating ram added, the steering wheel stops and the ram alters the oil flow into the flow valve, basically giving total control over the steering.

The main problem for John Hayward and Nick Key, who are working on the machine, involved the newly-machined rams. When

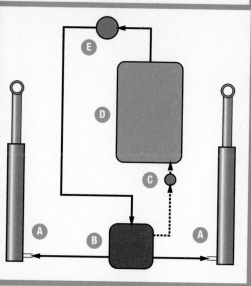

The steering system: A; hydraulic rams, B; flow control valve, C; return oil filter, D; oil tank, E; vane pump.

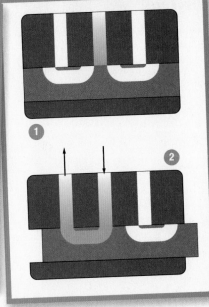

Sectional diagram of flow control valve: 1; oil flow - stationary, 2; oil to left-hand rams.

The hydraulic steering system's flow valve reducing tap.

the rear ram retracted, it blocked off the port back to the valve, preventing any further movement in the rams. This was soon remedied with a bit of extra machining by the ram manufacturers!

Not a problem - but more time consuming - were all the brackets that had to be measured and manufactured by John and Nick to carry the master and slave cylinders, plus routing the steel piping in between the two units.

GEARS

Four hand-operated levers control gear selection. The rear unit Hi-Low selection lever is as standard, while an additional lever operates a second Hi-Low lever ▶

The forward unit's Hi-Low gear stick and its two slave cylinders.

The forward unit's gear selector showing the linkages and return springs.

in the same way as a standard car.

The clutch has two master cylinders and a compensating link. The diff lock has a master and a slave. No slave cylinders are needed to return the clutch and diff lock slave cylinders as heavy-duty springs return the pedals.

STARTING AND STOPPING

Both units are controlled from the rear unit. The front unit's engine is started first by depressing the starting lever (as on a standard Fordson Major). This is to enable the driver to hear the front unit engine. Once this is running the rear unit is started by pressing a starting button. This button works in the same way as the Major's horn - depressing the button closes an electrical circuit thus engaging the front unit's starter motor. Both units have separate pull cables to cut the power to the engines.

Safety-wise both units have separate starter switches fitted and these must be turned on individually. Once the operator is in his seat all other controls can be operated, including shutting down both units.

THROTTLE

One throttle lever fitted on the rear unit's left-hand side works both engines via operating levers with a cable to the front engine. Along the system are adjusting screws. The front unit is set at a slightly higher rpm than the rear unit.

Bear in mind this article relates to the way Bernard's has been laid out. Positioning of the levers, master and slave cylinders has been set out by John Hayward and, although similar, these may differ to other Does.

on the front unit (shown above).

The rear unit's standard gear speeds are controlled by the usual selector shift but two levers are needed to control the front unit. The first lever moves the forward gearbox to select first to second, or third to reverse, while the second lever works the gate between first/second over to third/reverse and back.

Three slave cylinders control the forward gearbox (see top left of next page) in a similar way to the brakes on your car. One pushes the forward unit's gearlever down from first to second or third to reverse, the second slave pushes the opposite way while the third pushes the gear lever across from first/second through the gate to third/reverse. No slave is needed to push in the opposite direction here as two springs push against this third slave unit.

MORE SLAVES

The master slave cylinders (see top centre of next page) are filled with brake fluid. Depressing the lever or pedal forces the fluid from the master through brake piping to the slave cylinders, which in turn force a rod against the front unit's corresponding lever.

There are a total of seven slave cylinders operations:
1; Hi-Low gear lever up
2; Hi-Low gear lever down
3, 4, 5; Forward gearbox selectors
6; Clutch
7; Diff lock

The Hi-Low ratio gear lever has two slaves and these work in the same way as the gear lever.

Lift the rear unit's Hi-Low gear lever and a slave cylinder ram is operated on the front Doe unit. Lower the Hi-Low gear lever and the opposing slave ram is operated, forcing the slave lever to travel in the opposite direction. The slave cylinders are bled

A; hydraulic oil filter, B; offside steering ram and C; some of the master cylinders.

READY TO DANCE

Despite some minor setbacks, Bernard Saunders' tractor was finally running and went by low-loader to Allan Henshaw-Allcock's premises where, with help from Gary Barnard, it would have the tin work and electrics fitted.

It would be painted and ready for its first outing to the Newark and Nottinghamshire Agricultural Show as one of eight 'Dancing Does' in the show ring.

When it arrived at Allan's the machine was given a thorough check-over and assessed for "where to start."

Allan had worked on both engines while they were out of the Doe and, apart from a final tweaking to set the idle speeds, nothing more was needed here.

Two new radiators had been bought from Geoff Matthews Engineering near Chesterfield (01246 851118) and these were now fitted together with the hoses.

The original rear wings were badly worn but Allan brought these back to life while Gary refurbished the original wheels. Their centres were badly pitted but, with a great deal of effort, Gary managed to save them. Reinforcing plates were welded into the rims - the originals showing signs of cracking (probably the ▶

wheel nuts were tightened too much).

Gary primed and sprayed all four wheels and Bernard Saunders had new Goodyear tyres waiting to go on them.

With the cooling system in order, the Doe was steam-cleaned, the rams covered in masking tape and the tractor sprayed. Red oxide primer was used (and plenty of it) then a grey undercoat before the final coats of Empire Blue.

The tin work was fitted next and Allan and Gary found a problem. Although the bonnets and nose cones were new, they came from two different suppliers and, even with a lot of pulling and tugging, they wouldn't marry together.

The better bonnets were kept and nose cones ordered from the same supplier and the problem was sorted! The advice here is to use one supplier.

The headlights and instrument panels were put in place. I noted that although the original wings were used on the rear unit the new front wings had elongated holes where the fixing bolts were dropped. More than 40 years of engineering technology and round holes (as on the original wings) couldn't be trusted!

A point to watch when restoring Majors is the tachometer. The older Majors (up to the Minimec fuel pump) need a right-hand tachometer. That is, the clock's needle rests on the left and moves clockwise to the right. Minimec tachos move anti-clockwise, from right to left. Get it wrong and the needle

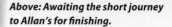

Above: Awaiting the short journey to Allan's for finishing.

Left: Gary puts a coat of blue on the front unit's engine.

Below: Gary's determination brought the original centres back as good as new.

stops working and you'll have 9999.9 hours on the clock in a split-second.

The wing lights had already been prepared and sprayed and everything was ready for wiring.

Mick Harrison is a self-employed auto-

electrician but started wiring the Doe, using the correct gauge wiring, old English colour-coded to the Fordson manual. He made his own looms for the Doe, although bulb

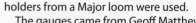

holders from a Major loom were used.

The gauges came from Geoff Matthews Engineering and once Allan fitted these in the panels Mick could get to work.

A word of caution here - Allan has fitted several Major looms (there are two sizes) and advises the restorer to double-check the connections using an electrical circuit tester.

Once Mick finished the wiring and tested it, the looms were wrapped in cloth tape to give the Doe the vintage touch.

The rear unit had the three horizontal bars across the nose cone, the front unit having standard Super Major grilles fitted

Left: Gary starts to replace the smaller fixtures and fittings on the rear unit.

(holes in for the headlights). The tin work had already been cleaned, primed and finished. All that was needed was a final touch-up once all the tin work was fitted.

One slight error that can and will be easily rectified is the Doe's grey wings. Ford Tractor Grey was used as a finishing colour. This was first used on the later pre-Force Fords (Ford 5000). The original colour was Fordson Tractor Grey, a slightly darker tone.

Once the final coat of paint was dry Allan started to double-check all the plugs, cotter pins and grease points, then Gary started up both engines (front first) and eased the Doe into the sunshine, where it was left to dry thoroughly before the badges were fitted.

On May 8, due to the hard-work - often well into the night- of John Hayward, Nick Key, Allan and Gary to name but four, serial number D330 duly took to the show ring at Newark with seven other Does to do a dance routine. ■

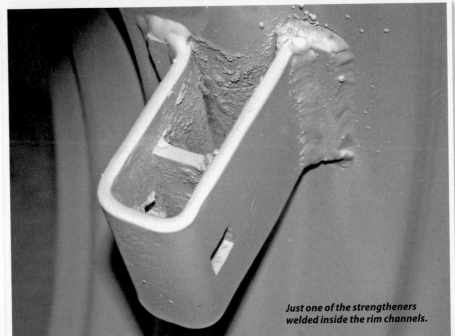

Just one of the strengtheners welded inside the rim channels.

serial number D330 duly took to the show ring at Newark with seven other Does to do a dance routine.

Bernard in the ring at the Newark and Notts Show in May.

John outdoes doe

Peter Squires meets The 170hp Beast

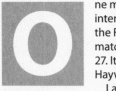

One machine caused more interest than most at the Flintham ploughing match on September 27. It was John Hayward's Triple Doe! Last year he altered the tractor to accommodate a Ford 6D six-cylinder engine in the rear unit, but this year he has gone a step further. The Doe has been given a power boost with a third engine, increasing the blue and orange 'beast' to around 170hp.

What made him do it?

"A friend commented after I'd fitted the six-cylinder engine, 'What's next, fit a third engine?' We laughed but then I thought about it, thought some more and then decided, why not? It can be done!"

In engineering there is no such word as can't, only when! John decided to keep the four-cylinder Major engine at the front and the 6D Ford at the rear, but added another front axle-less four-cylinder Major to the back, coupling it up via the pick-up hitch.

CONTROLS

The machine is driven from the middle, this being the original Triple Doe driving position. The two gauges have been re-routed to sit over the third Major's cowl so the driver can look over his shoulder and see them.

All the controls are operated from the central driving position. With all three engines running the foot clutch is depressed and the front two units put into gear. The rear unit has an over-centre clutch, fabricated by John and fitted on to a cradle above the rear nose cone. The hand clutch is operated and the third unit put into gear via two handles (Hi-Lo range selector and the main gearstick), which are also mounted on the cradle.

The foot clutch is lifted and the unit moves forward, the rear hitch being lowered via another handle on the cradle, and the 21-tine cultivator lowered into the ground via the heavy-duty lift rams that John made in the style of Doe as the original Major lift arms could not cope. The arms lift the cultivator using a modest 500psi, only a fifth of the Major's 2,500psi hydraulic capacity.

Once the tractor is moving, the driver reaches behind and drops the over-centre clutch handle to bring the third (rear) unit into play. All three units are now working in harness and what a beautiful sound they make!

As the machine reaches the end of the field the cultivator is lifted clear and the rear unit hand clutch is depressed. With only the front two driving units now operational the tractor is turned round ready to head back up the field.

SIZE IMPRESSES

At Flintham Thomas Waterhouse seemed to be making light work operating John's unique machine, while John was kept busy answering questions from spectators. The beast's size was further emphasised by the fact that John had added twin wheels to the centre and rear driving axles. Three engines, 14 cylinders, ten wheels, one driver - and a very long garage to keep it in!

When John's friend asks him what's next, he already has the answer:

"A V8 engine in the rear unit."

To some, this may seem daft, but not to John. The rear unit on a Triple Doe is where the most power should come from to work the implement, hence the reason for putting the six-cylinder engine in last year.

With a four-cylinder third engine being added to the rear unit, the six-cylinder engine is now central. So with a V8 in the rear unit, six-cylinder in the middle and four cylinders at the front, John should have a winner.

1. *Double handle: Clutch (In-out)*
2. *Double handle: Linkage (Raise-lower)*
3. *Single handle: Gears (Range - Hi-low)*
4. *Single handle: Gears (Speed)*

SAFETY IS PARAMOUNT

Safety was foremost when he planned this project. What if the rear unit jack-knifed into the central unit, or the centre unit cut out and the rear unit carried on?

First of all, John designed the machine so that the rear unit could not be started unless the centre unit was already running. Also, if the centre unit cut out, the rear unit would automatically cut out.

Jack-knifing? The rear unit is coupled to a telescopic drawbar. Once the drawbar's spring is triggered by the rear unit pushing into it, the rear unit cuts out automatically.

And if you do question this project, try and imagine the first comments directed at Ernest Doe and the first impressions of his weird pair of Fordson Majors, permanently coupled together with no front axle, snaking in the middle.

I can imagine a good element of derision at the time, until the 100hp machine proved its worth in the field. Yet all Ernest Doe was trying to do was to take tractors into the 100hp four-wheel drive bracket.

Bearing all this in mind, look again at what John has done. He has used his skills to move a stage further from the original concept. ■

Thomas Waterhouse takes the helm. With this much power available, the machine makes light work of operating the 21-tine cultivator, even in heavy soil conditions. The combination of horsepower, traction and manoeuvrability make it an awesome spectacle.

The Beast's rear unit is coupled to the centre unit via this neatly fabricated, telescopic drawbar. This enables easy coupling/uncoupling should the rear unit need to be removed.

The rear unit's linkage is pure Doe - two assistor rams help to lift the cultivator.

Double Dexta Design

Dave Beare follows the creation of a mini Triple-D

Dexta devotee Graham Morris had a dream. Being a Dexta enthusiast with a collection of a baker's dozen of Fordson's finest is one way of enjoying the marque, but what could a Dexta collector aspire to when he has already searched for and found (or created) many of the 4x4 versions he looked for?

For many enthusiasts of the Fordson marque in general, one of the most desirable tractors is one of Mr Doe's Triple-Ds, the fantastic articulated twin-Fordson Major devised by George Pryor and Ernest Doe in the 1950s to get to grips with heavy ploughing necessary for cultivating some of the heaviest soils in Britain.

Unfortunately, these days even a rough but genuine Triple-D is going to cost a lot of money, tens of thousands just for an incomplete wreck with as much again and then some to turn it into a decent running machine. Not to mention the need for some serious storage and workshop space to accommodate it.

Why not take a different approach?

Fordson Dextas are still relatively affordable, much less stratospheric than Triple Ds, and still fairly easy to come by. Would it be possible to devise an articulated Dexta along the lines of a Doe?

It would, indeed, and for Graham Morris it became a dream which he did something about. He already had a couple of good-condition Super Dextas which would serve as a basis for a unique creation, so he shared his ideas with Andy Belfield, a neighbour, farmer and talented engineer from nearby Llandridod Wells in mid-Wales.

Graham offered Andy the two good-condition Super Dextas and some thoughts on how he imagined a Tandem Dexta could be made. The die was cast. Both tractors were transported to Andy's workshop, lined up one behind the other and studied from all angles to decide how to carry out such a complex conversion.

As with Ernie Doe's original Triple-D, the vital parts of an articulated double-tractor are the central turntable, steering mechanism and hydraulic controls between the front and rear units, allowing a tight turning-circle and management of the front unit from the driver's seat at the rear.

The Doe has a simple flat disc centre turntable but a sophisticated twin hydraulic ram steering gear which allows an almost 90 degree articulation, giving a tighter turning-circle than the standard Fordson Major. The Dexta Tandem Tractor has a similar arrangement, ingeniously using the central articulation from a Benford dumper truck with welded-on support frames. The centre unit gives a bit less articulation than a Doe but still a tight-enough turning circle; it also allows axial rotation of the two units - the bonnet of the rear tractor can almost touch the wings of the front one.

Steering is operated via an orbital valve feeding a pair of hydraulic rams per side, supplied from the front Dexta's trailer-tipping high pressure system, and is light and direct without being too high-geared.

The front unit is completely controlled from the driver's seat on the rear unit, including starting and stopping, clutch, gear changing and braking, all achieved through a total of nine hydraulic master and eight slave cylinders, working through 80 feet of pipework! A further 20 feet are of high-grade stainless braided hose.

Andy Belfield probably spent as much

Graham Morris drives the Tandem on its first public outing, demonstration-ploughing at the 2008 All-Wales match.

Left: Hard at work with the Tandem and Ransomes TS 70 four-furrow plough.

Andy that it's impossible to see the join.

Early testing showed the need for a lot of extra weight on the rear wheels, not only to achieve optimum traction but because it was found that on full-lock (eg to the left) the right rear wheel could almost be lifted off the ground manually, such was the weight transfer! Doe's Triple-Ds suffered from similar characteristics.

The Tandem Tractor is a highly successful engineering adventure - Andy Belfield and Graham Morris have created a unique machine which not only looks fabulous but is very capable and, had it been developed many years ago before the advent of mainstream 4x4 tractors from big manufacturers, could have been every bit as successful as a hard-working farm tractor as the now much-coveted Triple-D. ∎

time perfecting the control system as he did on the rest of the conversion - most complex of all the controls was devising an accurate gear-change system for the front unit. It paid off handsomely because, during a short test run, everything between front and rear Dextas was well-synchronised and a driver with no previous experience (me) was soon at ease.

Another extraordinary fact about the Tandem Tractor is that work began with two unmodified Dextas in January 2008 and I was driving the machine, fully sorted, in August 2008, an incredibly short time

given the complexity of such a project.

Demonstration ploughing at Hindwell Farm during the 2008 All-Wales match at Hindwell Farm proved what a capable machine the Tandem is, and it certainly attracted a lot of attention. Coupled to a Ransomes TS 70 four-furrow plough the Tandem simply dug in and took off, no wheel-slip at all and the throttles barely open. It could have handled much more demanding conditions with ease and a lot more speed.

The two Super Dexta engines muster 88hp between them and all of it is usable; traction on the front unit is phenomenal with all that weight bearing on oversize wheels and tyres. Wheels are Claas combine harvester rims with the centres cut out and Dexta centres welded in so well by

Top: Gear change and clutch master cylinders on the rear unit...

Above: ... and corresponding slave cylinders on the front unit.

A lot of plumbing! Hydraulic connections between front and rear units.

ALL GRIP TRACTION

Graham & David Morris can be contacted at All Grip Traction, Henllys Farm, Cwnbach, Builth Wells LD2 3RW (01982 553791 or 07971 356970) and if you fancy your own Tandem Tractor, Andy Belfield can be contacted at Belfield Engineering, Llandrindod Wells (01597 823992).

Major Electrical Connections

On a recent working visit to a large fruit-growing estate in deepest Herefordshire Alan Watson came across an unusual Fordson Major which can still be called upon to rescue modern day tractors.

As you travel around shows, rallies or working events across the length and breadth of Great Britain and Ireland you will see many tractors restored to a very high standard as well as some unusual looking models still in their 'working clothes'. As we all know, many tractors have been changed from the original purpose and converted for various operations over the years. These conversions can often be a great source of interest among tractor enthusiasts.

Even today, with tractors now recognised as early classics commanding high prices at auction there are still many quality tractors and conversions based on farms, still working and no-one, apart from the farm staff, ever get to see such interesting machines.

Alan says "Whilst repairing some machinery on a fruit farm recently, I had occasion to go into the big tractor shed. There, to my surprise, was a very unusual Fordson Major painted in duck egg blue. It had a Boughton winch on the rear and a strange looking framework around the cab roof. After I had finished the work that

It is surprising how many interesting tractors designed for specific tasks are still called upon for work today.

The original rated plates are still fixed to the rear mudguards of the tractor.

I had been called in to do, I asked the Farm Manager a few general questions about the Major and asked if I would be allowed to take some photographs.

Happily he answered my questions and took the tractor out of the shed so I could take these photographs."

It transpires that this particular Fordson had major electrical connections - in every sense! It spent much of its working life with the South Wales Electricity Board. The main operation for this tractor was for winching electric lines over hilly terrain and across the open fields of the shire counties of Hereford, Gloucester and Worcester. This explained the fitting of the Boughton winch.

'One thing that did puzzle me was the strange square framework around the cab roof. After a hasty phone call by the Farm Manager it appears it was no more than a simple protection guard. When the Electricity Board was winching cables and setting new pylon lines the crew often had to go through woodland, deep scrub and hedge backs. To this end, the

Fitted with a P-W17 Boughton winch with a safe working load of 15,000 lbs direct pull, the Major was used to winch cable over the rolling countryside by the South Wales Electricity Board.

Major was called on to winch and extract timber, and the square frame was simply a way of moving low hanging branches away from the operator's cab to avoid cab and window damage" explained Alan.

Around 30 years ago, the present owner of this tractor saw the decommissioned Major in one of the SWEB's yards and thought what a useful machine it could be on his own farm. Even though most

of the farm's land is rich, fertile and easily workable there is a pocket of low-lying land which is peaty and in wet times it has been known for tractors to become bogged down. There were numerous problems when trying to retrieve machines from the suction of the bog.

The set-up on the Fordson enables the Major to anchor itself on firm going and use the Boughton winch, which has nearly 50 yards of steel cable, to retrieve trapped machines without becoming stuck itself. The last time it was used in this situation was in the autumn of 2007 when it had to pull a tractor and trailer out of a potato field, the tractor had broken through the bog surface down to the underlying peat. Seemingly without effort the Major winched the modern combination out of its potential watery grave and onto terra-firma.

When the Major with the electrical connections is not in use recovering vehicles, the large arable estate often uses it for winching timber out of its many woodlands and occasionally neighbours ask to borrow the machine for some of their own work.

This tractor is doubtless one of many that still retain enormous value to their owners as working machines. As such, they are unlikely to make public appearances. If such machines were ever to be sold to enthusiasts, what would the seller do for an alternative?

Very few farmers can claim to have access to such cheap, easy to maintain machines that have cost very little.

There is no logic to selling a valuable workhorse and replacing it with a much more expensive machine. ∎

It is believed the square framework on the cab roof was added to deflect overhanging branches when the tractor worked close to hedgerows and woodland.

History of a ploughman

WT (Tom) Hooper left a unique record, as Gary Boyd-Hope discovers

Tom (front row, third right) wrestles with an armful of trophies following a successful trip to the Halesowen and Hagley Farmers Club match in November 1955.

The line-up of silverware on the sideboard at home gives an indication of Tom's success as a match ploughman.

A superb photo of Tom making the opening cut, or 'cop', at Halesowen in 1955. No doubt the days leading up to the show were spent meticulously measuring and adjusting the plough.

Tom's Fordson Standard, registration ENP 614;, and the Ransomes, Sims and Jeffries match plough were familiar sights at events throughout Worcestershire in the 1950s. Here the trailing boats define Tom's superb furrows at Hanbury in 1957.

Tom;, the Standard Fordson and the Ransomes match plough head for victory at the Chaddesley Corbett and District Farmers Club match in 1958.

Tom tended to enter local matches only;, but did partake in a handful of national events. In a Class Two national match in Taunton during October 1963;, all competitors were given the use of a brand new Fordson Super Major and here Tom gets to grips with his new steed.

T om Hooper left a unique record of his life because he simply kept everything.

Now his son John has mountains of newspaper cuttings, invoices, receipts, photographs, calendars, you name it - if it related to Tom's business, he kept hold of it.

As I sifted through the papers it emerged that, apart from being a businessman, Tom was an exceptional ploughman with a string of match titles under his belt.

The family agricultural contractors business had begun in 1935 when Tom's mother Mabel, trading as M Hooper, set up a thrashing and cultivation contracting business at Chadwich Grange near Rubery, Worcestershire.

Tom and his brother Robert did most of the physical work, including a lot of horse ploughing and, following Mabel's death, the brothers took over the running of the firm.

Eventually, however, the brothers decided to go their separate ways and Tom acquired The Holdings, a mediumsized smallholding on Wildmoor Lane in Wildmoor, Bromsgrove.

The business was very successful, and Tom and his gang harvested and ploughed huge tracts of the Worcestershire countryside in the days when farms had less acreage than the 'super-fanns' of today. When young John left school and joined his dad in the business, Tom was operating around a dozen tractors (mostly of Ford origin) and a fleet of Ransomes, Sims and Jeffries conventional and reversible ploughs.

When it came to ploughing, Tom had very high standards and hated to see a poorly ploughed field. He developed the skill from the age of 12 with a horse team and later used Standard Fordsons, a Case machine and an Oliver 80.

He entered numerous matches in the area, using a Standard Fordson which he had stripped down and rebuilt completely, ensuring that it worked perfectly. ▶

Looking at the furrows to the right of this photograph, it is little wonder that Tom Hooper dominated West Midlands ploughing matches for so long.

The quality of the turned earth, with no sign of stubble and nicely broken up, was typical of Tom Hooper when working with a digger bodied plough. He is pictured here at Chaddesley Corbett in 1962.

This was never used for day-to-day ploughing, only for matches.

The Fordson was paired with a Ransomes match plough and John remembers the amount of time and effort his father spent before every match ensuring that the plough was set exactly right.

The routine would start days before each event when Tom would get out the match equipment and start measuring the level of the plough, checking the alignment and the pitch, setting the width of cut, ensuring that the 'boats' were free to move and generally making sure that both the plough and tractor were spotless.

This attention to appearance carried over into the business and on one occasion when a driver returned to The Holdings after a long day ploughing with the plough still caked in dirt, Tom sent him back to the field and told him not to return until the plough was clean.

Once the measurements were set, Tom's match preparations would then see him take the tractor and plough into a neighbour's field and practise the opening, or 'copping', and then carry out some practice runs to see how the soil was turning.

After a few runs the measurements were taken again, adjusted where necessary, and then another driver would take the wheel while Tom walked behind to check the quality of the ploughing. Again adjustments would be made and this went on until Tom was completely happy with the equipment.

All that remained then was to get the tractor and plough loaded up and ready to go, along with a set of spade-lug wheels in case the going turned out to be tough on the day of the match.

It may sound a little extreme, but the trophies on Tom's sideboard proved that his high standards really paid off.

Looking at just some of the newspaper cutting which John has, you get a strong impression of just how skilful Tom was at match ploughing. The 1963 Bromsgrove and District Farmers Club event was something of a double victory for the Hoopers as not only did Tom emerge as champion, but John also won a Young Farmers Club award for being best junior ploughman. There's no doubt Tom was a skilled ploughman

and he encouraged his workforce to take as much pride in the task as he did.

One of his employees, a Welshman named Tom Banning, certainly had the gift and became a top ploughman himself.

After Tom Hooper sold his Case tractor and bought a County crawler, Tom Banning would spend around eight months of the year ploughing and was able to give his boss a run for his money.

At one club match the two Toms went head-to-head in a members' and employees' competition, with Tom Banning on the County with a Ransomes crawler plough behind. He won, out-ploughing the man who had taught him everything he knew.

Tom Hooper was a ploughman through and through and remained so until John took over the running of the business in the 1980s.

It was tough work, especially when the weather turned cold and he was sat at the wheel of a cabless tractor for days at a time, but John recalls it with affection.

The Hoopers remained loyal to Ford and Fordson tractors over the years, with the last one - a Ford 66 - joining the fleet in 1984. In the mid-1990s John called it a day, although he still has the Ford 66.

He also has all of his dad's clipping and photos, making a fabulous record of one man's career. ∎

SOME OF HIS TITLES INCLUDE:

1950: hagley Farmers Club Annual Show, Best Ploughing award

1951: Forest of Arden Agricultural Society, Match Plough winner

1955: Halesowen and Hagley Farmers Club, Open Tractor Challenge Cup, Bristol Street Motors Cup, Ransomes, Sims and Jeffries Award

1956: Forest of Arden Agricultural Society, Lucas Challenge Cup champion Halesowen and Hagley Farmers Club, Open Tractor Challenge Cup, Bristol Street Motors Cup, Ransomes, Sims and Jeffries Award Chaddesley Corbett Farmers Club, Open Ploughingchampion

1957: Halesowen and Hagley Farmers Club, Open Tractor Challenge Cup, Ransomes, Sims and Jeffries Award Droitwich and Bromsgrove Club, Open Challenge champion Chaddesley Corbett Farmers Club, Open Ploughing champion

1958: Chaddesley Corbett Farmers Club, Open Ploughing champion

1962: Chaddesley Corbett Farmers Club, Tractor Ploughing champion

1963: Bromsgrove and District Club, ploughing champion

JCB MkI

Dedicated JCB enthusiast Tim Starkey-Smith.

Over the years, Ford and Fordson tractors have been linked with many innovative companies, one of which was J. C. Bamford of Rocester. Tim Starkey-Smith explained his interest in the Fordson Majorbased early JCB machines.

T im was born in Oxford where he lived until he was nine years old. His father was in the RAF so, inevitably, the family moved several times, spending time at Wantage, RAF Valley in Anglesey and also in Germany. He finished his schooling in Wales when his father returned to RAF Valley and then completed a YTS course on a local farm. When the family moved to Stafford, Tim worked on farms in Brewood and Dunston.

"As a child I was always fascinated with diggers," said Tim "and working on farms with old JCBs around fuelled my interest even more, so I began studying these old machines."

Some people are fortunate enough to be able to combine their hobby with their working life and in 1988 Tim successfully applied for a job as a trainee digger driver. Six of the last 18 years were spent working as a test driver for JCB.

He is also the proud owner of several Fordson-based JCB excavators, including a Mk1 and a Hydra- Digga Loadall 65.

RARE BEAST

Tim's 1954 JCB Mk1 is quite a rare beast. Based on a Fordson Major, the Mk1 was the first mainstream production digger built by J. C. Bamford. Around 550 were built between 1954 and 1957, when they were superseded by the Hydra-Digga. The Mk1 was available as a backhoe with a front-mounted ballast weight, a backhoe-loader or a backhoecompressor.

Tim explained: "There were only about seven machines fitted with the compressor, the remainder being split between the other two variants. As far as I am aware, of around 20 known surviving Mk1 machines, this is the only backhoe-compressor." The hydraulic excavator has a reach of 16 feet, will dig to a depth of 11 feet and was available with a range of bucket widths to suit many tasks. It has a geared pump, which is crankshaftdriven and double-acting cylinders with chrome-plated piston rods to eliminate wear. With a height of 12 feet 6 inches, it could load to a higher diggers. When the 'A' frame is lowered, the width of the base can be extended to 15 feet 6 inches to give extra stability in working conditions, which JCB claimed was a safety feature unique to its machines. ▶

Technical specification

Model	JCB Mk1
Year of manufacture	1954
Produced between	1954-1957
Number made	550
Excavator Reach	16 feet
Dig Depth	11 feet
Load Height	12 feet 6 inches
Tractor	**Fordson E1A Major**
Engine Ford	4 cylinder diesel
Displacement	220 cu in
Bore and Stroke	3.937 inches x 4.52 inches
Transmission	4f 2r
Compressor	**Holman**
Model	TA13
Produced	1960s
Displacement	130cu ft per minute
Pressure	100psi
Revolutions	1250rpm
Power Requirement	28hp

JACK HAMMERS

The compressor fitted to the front of the machine is a Holman 'T' type which was used to power two pneumatic jack hammers to break the surface of a trench in front of the machine. The backhoe would then be used to dig it out. Holman Brothers Ltd, established by Nicholas Holman in 1801, manufactured this particular compressor unit during the 1950s and 1960s. The company manufactured pneumatic tools and was based in Camborne, Cornwall, and is now part of CompAir, one of the world leaders in manufacturing compressed air and gas systems.

Tim said: "I bought the Mk1 in 2002 from Reg Dury of Salisbury. It was supplied new to a building company in Cornwall called Rogers and Christian. So far, I have managed to trace it back to the 1980s, but it would be nice to be able to build up a complete history." It was actually in two pieces when he bought it, the tractor and compressor as one unit and the excavator another.

Fortunately the Fordson Major itself required only general maintenance work. The brakes were checked and adjusted. However, Tim did find one potentially big problem, the engine oil had emulsified which could have meant that water was getting into the oil, indicating possible problems with the head gasket, or worse – casting damage: "After a couple of oil changes, it came clear so I can only assume that it was bad oil. It has been fine since then."

BAD CORROSION

The compressor was also working, but Tim doesn't need to use it when showing his machine. However, he may have the tank professionally tested as he says it would be handy for blowing tyres up! The 'A' frame and excavator assembly was a different matter though. The whole of the bottom of the 'A'

Tim found his rare Mk1 in Salisbury in 2002 and is now trying to trace its history.

frame and the outriggers were badly corroded so the whole assembly had to be replaced.

The hollow box section of the boom was also found to be in quite a bad state when it was dismantled. Rather than repair it, Tim decided to replace the structure to make a stronger job.

He also replaced the tin cladding, which was missing when he bought it. Several of the pins in the rams were seized in place, so these were cut and replaced. "RAF Engineering & Hydraulic Services in Birmingham worked on all the rams last year," Tim said. "Some were reconditioned, but three were completely re-built from

scratch." All hydraulic hoses were replaced and the valve block was reconditioned. RAF Engineering had to make new spindles to operate the spools which operate the hydraulics. Tim fitted filters to the side of the oil tank to protect the system as some of the Mk1 machines were not fitted with these.

A MAJOR PROBLEM

Topmarc Ltd of Hixon carried out structural repairs to the steelwork of the digger. One major problem discovered on re-assembly was with the mounting bracket connecting the tractor to the excavator. The bracket had been repaired in the past and had been made too narrow to accommodate the top link on the digger. It took four weeks to repair the excavator and 'A' frame and it was all finally completed just before Tim was to take it to a show!

Tim is very proud of his 1954 JCB Mk1, one of 550 built between 1954 and 1957. The Fordson Major-based JCB Mk1 was available in three variants but only about seven were fitted with the Holman model 'T' compressor.

Boom slewing is operated by a hydraulically-controlled rack and pinion.

There were only about seven JCB Mk1 machines fitted with the compressor.

The hydraulic pump is mounted on the front of the crankshaft and the compressor is driven from the normal belt pulley.

The 'A' frame and outriggers were badly corroded, so Tim has had to replace the whole assembly.

The 'T' type compressor was manufactured by Holman in the 1950s and 60s. Holman is now part of CompAir, one of the world leaders in compressed air and gas systems.

However, Tim still needed to source badges for the cladding on the boom. He observed: "The two pairs of badges were cast out of aluminium as that seemed to be the material used on an original badge borrowed from a friend who was also restoring a Mk1.

This was used as a pattern to cast my two 'JCB' badges. The two 'Excavator' badges required a bit more ingenuity. I had photographed a Mk1 with both sets of badges on six years ago and I also had the dimensions of the plate.

After discussing how to make a pattern, my friend Phil came up with the idea of using plastic letters from car number plates and mounting them on a suitable backing, in this case MDF. After scaling up the photo I realised that the letters were quite accurately sized. When the finished badges came back the results exceeded all expectations!"

This very interesting machine attends local shows and also appears at the exhibitions which Tim helps to organise at the JCB factory at Rocester.

He did hint at another historic purchase he has recently made – but that's a story for another day! ■

Tim borrowed a JCB badge from a friend as a pattern for his machine, but a little more ingenuity was required for the 'Excavator' badge!

Bob's Nottinghamshire Trio!

Peter squires visited Bob Adam of Retford to find out why he is more than happy with his trio of Nottinghamshire Fordson Tractors, one of which he bought brand new in 1962

FLEET PROFILE · 165 SRR1963 Super Dexta · 849 MAL1962 Super Major · 699 AVO1958 Power Major

Bob Adam left school in 1954 to follow a career in agriculture. He studied at Brackenhurst Agricultural College, now part of Nottingham Trent University, where he gained his National Certificate in Agriculture in 1957. In 1960 he bought his 50-acre farm near Retford, Nottinghamshire, where he still lives with his wife Isabel. As the business developed, more land was acquired and the farm grew to 280 acres. Up to 130 acres of land was at any one time used to grow 'Record' potatoes to fulfil a contract with Walkers Crisps. Although Bob retired from farming in 1999 he still owns 100 acres which are rented by a neighbouring farmer.

In 1962 Bob purchased a brand-new Super Major from local Fordson dealer, Brooks of Newark, to replace the smaller Fordson Dexta, which was the first tractor Bob used when he moved to the farm. "We fitted a Nicholson front-mounted side hoe to the Super Major. This was 100 inches wide, and covered five rows at 20in widths. The cast front wheel centres had to be changed for pressed steel centres as the pressure on the tyres from the working hoe would blow them," said Bob.

A real workhorse

The tractor was also fitted with a Horndraulic loader mainly used for loading sugar beet. Bob says that the Major was a real workhorse, recording 9,000 hours on the clock during its working life. As the farm's acreage grew the Super Major was relegated to the back of the shed where it remained untouched for nearly 20 years until 2002.

More 'Power' to the farm

Bob's 1958 Power Major, fitted with a Mil loader, was bought in 1970 from a sale held by J. T. Stacey, a local threshing contractor based at nearby Markham Moor. Arthur Sanderson Tractors the main Fordson dealer had supplied the Major brand new to J. T. Stacey who at the time was based at Tuxford, three miles away. Arthur Sanderson Tractors later became Harris, then Platts Harris which is still going strong today as a New Holland dealer. The Power Major joined the Super Major on the farm, but was also relegated to the back of the shed when an increase in tractor power and performance was required.

On board the 1958 Power Major next to a copper-nailed clinker-built rowing boat.

Restoration

"When I retired in 1999 I became interested in the vintage tractor scene and decided to get the Super Major out of the shed and have a look at it," Bob explained. "It took me a year to restore the Super Major and this rekindled my interest in classic tractors. Jim Hoyland, who was a former Platts Harris man, reconditioned the engine for me. With his mechanical experience it was the sensible thing to do. Most of the other work I have completed myself. The rear trumpet housing seals were replaced, but apart from that the tractor needed nothing new except rear lights. The light surrounds were original and I was able to buy new lenses from Steve

Perryman in St Austell."

He continued: "When the Horndraulic loader was taken off, I found that all those years of lifting had cracked one of the chassis side frames on the Super Major, so I had that repaired. Loader strain had also worn the trunnion pin hole about two-thirds through; again this was repaired and re-machined to size. I decided to keep the original cast Nicholson side-hoe brackets that we fitted to the front axle of the Super Major. The cowl had one or two dents in it where sugar beet had fallen from the loader, but I left these and sprayed over them. Well, it is a bit of mine and the tractor's history," laughed Bob.

The next restoration project was the

Bob's Power Major was relegated to ashed when more horsepower was needed on the farm. It has now been restored to its former glory.

Power Major and apart from a bit of cutting and welding to the rear wings the tractor did not need a great deal of work doing to bring it back to its former glory; it still has the original radiator. As with the Super Major, the Power Major was fitted with replacement rear trumpet housing seals.

Electrical repairs

"FFA member Paul Hird carried out work to the electrical wiring system on the Power Major," explained Bob who went on to say: "Paul has also recently restored

Power Major, registration number 981 AVO, which is a difference of only 282 numbers to mine."

The final Fordson to be restored was a 1963 Super Dexta, which had also been supplied new by Arthur Sanderson Tractors to Clarence Howcroft of Ordsall near Retford in Nottinghamshire. Bob bought it from Clarence's son Graham five years ago.

"The tractor had hardly ventured off Clarence's farm, so had not been taxed for many years. Yet the original buff logbook was found, which meant that I could retain ▶

Bob Adam aboard his 1962 Super Major, bought new to replace the smaller Fordson Dexta with Bob's next project, a three-ton Nicholson Leaway tipping trailer.

Bob with his 1963 Super Dexta.

of the filler cap! Restoration of the Super Dexta was relatively easy, and the only problem I encountered was starting the Perkins engine. I had carried out all the work on it, but once back together it wouldn't start. At first, a drop of 'Easy Start' appeared to solve the problem and it seemed to cure itself after that. Perhaps it just needed a little encouragement."

The hydraulic lift on the Dexta would not operate correctly and after scratching his head Bob found that the problem had been caused by the hydraulic control valve, which was sticking. Once cleaned of all the rust that had built up over the years, the hydraulics operated correctly.

Next project

As a member of the NVTEC Nottinghamshire Group, Bob shows his tractors at the club's Working Weekend and attends other local events. The Super Major took part in the inaugural 'Ducksbury Charity Road Run' in July 2006, which covered some 40 miles in and around the

Tuxford area.

Bob doesn't think he will buy any more tractors having restored the three he owns. But there is another restoration project on the horizon; an original three-ton.

Nicholson Leaway tipping trailer, serial number A/0166, purchased from Ray Bingley of Clarborough in 1966 and used for carting grain and sugar beet. The trailer more than looked the part, coupled up to Bob's Super Major in front of the farm. ∎

the original registration number and tax it for road use." Bob says that Clarence was quite a character and recalls one of many stories Clarence used to tell him: "There was

a lad who worked for him who was a bit naive. The Dexta needed some engine oil in it, so Clarence told the lad to fill it up.

Apparently he did, right up to the top

Scraper Major

Michael O'Regan from Knockaderry in County Limerick, Republic of Ireland, writes: "This 1956 E1A Fordson Major is used solely for yard scraping duties and wouldn't look the same without its scraper as they have been attached for such a long time.

"It's fitted with a four-cylinder engine from a Ford D Series truck, which starts easily every time."

Vernon Wyke from Minsterley in Shropshire says this faithful machine starts first time and cleans up after 200 cows morning and night.

The family has had the 1955 Fordson Major since 1963 and it started its scraping career in 1967. Due to corrosion it has had four replacement wheel centres and two engines, says Vernon.

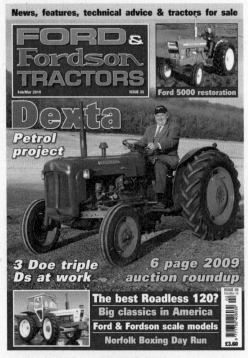